DAILY CLOSE-UPS FOR WINTER

Written by Mary Magaldi, Bruce Russell, and Carol Olsgard

Edited by Connie Flesner
Illustrated by Robyn Hall

Cover by Gary Mohrmann

GOOD APPLE, INC.
BOX 299
CARTHAGE, IL 62321-0299

TABLE OF CONTENTS

INTRODUCTION

Welcome to *Daily Close-Ups for Winter.* We hope you will enjoy these activities to supplement or enhance your daily lessons. This book is divided into three units—December, January, and February. Each unit contains twenty-six pages of activities that are based on actual events in history. Each month contains a calendar and a page describing possible ways for the students to use the calendar. You will also find suggestions on using the calendar as a basis for a bulletin board as well as patterns for cutouts that can be decorated and used by the students.

These pages were designed so that you, the teacher, would have an activity for students to do while you are busy taking roll, lunch count, lunch money, etc. Some activities may take the student much longer and perhaps could be used when he/she is finished with other assignments during the day. You, as the teacher, will best know how to use these pages for your students.

I hope you will enjoy this book as much as I have enjoyed editing it. If you like *Daily Close-Ups for Winter,* please note that *Daily Close-Ups for Fall* and *Daily Close-Ups for Spring* are also available from Good Apple.

Good luck and have fun!

Connie Flesner

DECEMBER

It came upon
  a stormy night.
The stars were shining
  very bright.
The pines were
  letting out their scent,
As if they knew
  what Christmas meant.
Then came a new
  and shiny morn,
When the sun
  was very warm.
You should have seen
  the pretty sight,
By long, last flickering
  candlelight.

*Sharon
Age 9*

December

Sunday	Monday	Tuesday	Wednesday	Thursday	Friday	Saturday

A. Run off enough calendars on the opposite page so that each student can have one of his own. You may also want to reproduce the cutouts found at the bottom of this page. The student can use these cutouts as "stickers" for his calendar. If one side of the pattern is put on the fold and the rest is cut out, the student can lift the pattern and write on the inside. These cutout "stickers" can be decorated as the student wishes. The cutout can be taped or glued to the appropriate place on the calendar.

The following activities are suggested uses for the calendar:

1. Have students put a Christmas custom from another country on the calendar each day.
2. Have a different student record the snowfall for each day. Have him predict if it will be a white Christmas.
3. Explain to the students that Christmas is the season of giving and sharing. Each day a different student can write down a way to share a gift from the heart. For instance visiting someone in the nursing home is a good way to give of yourself.

B. Enlarge the calendar (on the opposite page) to design a bulletin board for your classroom. An example is shown above. You may want students to complete ongoing activities to fill in the calendar. One student can be assigned to a specific day of the month. Some suggestions are given below. Enlarge the cutout patterns for students to write down the information they wish to place on the calendar. If one side of the pattern is put on the fold and the rest is cut out, the student can lift the pattern and write on the inside. These cutout "stickers" can be decorated as the student wishes. The cutout can be taped or glued to the appropriate place on the calendar.

1. Each student can make a report about Christmas trees. Information such as how the tradition got started, where Christmas trees are grown, safety involved, etc., should be included. The calendar can be a countdown to a decorated Christmas tree. Each day the student should write down one direction for decorating the tree. (For example, day 1—select a good tree; day 2—put it in a tree stand with water; day 3—add the lights, etc.)
2. Each student can make a countdown until Christmas day. Every day he should write down something he has to do to prepare for Christmas (go shopping, sing carols, etc.).

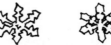

ACTIVITIES FOR DECEMBER

CHECK THE OIL, PLEASE

The first drive-in automobile service station was opened by the Gulf Refining Company on December 1, 1913, in Pittsburgh, Pennsylvania. The station remained open all night and gave free crankcase service.

Read the car mileage chart below. It shows gas mileage you would get for one gallon of gasoline doing city driving or doing highway driving with various cars. Read and compute the problems below.

 **CAR MILEAGE CHART**

Kind of car	City driving— miles per gallon	Highway driving— miles per gallon
A. Cadillac Coupe de Ville	15	22
B. Ford LTD	20	26
C. Volkswagen Rabbit	27	40
D. Datsun	39	50

1. Four people driving cars A, B, C, and D, each traveled 60 city miles a week. How many gallons of gas will each driver use? (Round your answer to second decimal.)

   Driver A uses _____ gal.   Driver C uses _____ gal.

   Driver B uses _____ gal.   Driver D uses _____ gal.

2. These same drivers travel 300 highway miles a week. How many gallons of gas does each driver use on highway driving a week?

   Driver A uses _____ gal.   Driver C uses _____ gal.

   Driver B uses _____ gal.   Driver D uses _____ gal.

3. What is the total gallons of gas used by each driver for one week (both city and highway miles)?

   Driver A uses _____ gal.   Driver C uses _____ gal.

   Driver B uses _____ gal.   Driver D uses _____ gal.

4. If gas costs $1.05 per gallon, how much would each driver spend per week for gas (both city and highway traveling)?

   Driver A spends _____ per week   Driver C spends _____ per week

   Driver B spends _____ per week   Driver D spends _____ per week

5. On the back do the four problem steps with a driver of a Buick car getting 18 city miles per gallon and 25 highway miles per gallon.

LONG DISTANCE "I DO'S"

The telephone has given us many ways to make our lives easier. We can call long distances to talk to anyone we need to. On December 2, 1933, two people used the telephone to perform the first transatlantic telephone wedding.

Making calls over long distances will give you a big phone bill. Look at the phone bill below and answer the questions.

Date	Time	To Place	Minutes	Amount
12-1	1:30 p.m.	New York City	14	$ 3.95
12-4	7:30 p.m.	Small Town, AZ	22	14.92
12-11	8:00 a.m.	Salt Lake City, UT	17	7.83
12-15	9:16 a.m.	Phoenix, AZ	12	9.60
12-20	2:30 p.m.	Dallas, TX	19	5.66
12-24	12:00 a.m.	North Pole	5	32.09

1. On what day was a call made to the North Pole? _____

2. What time was a call made to Phoenix, Arizona? _____

3. How much did the call to Small Town, Arizona, cost? _____

4. How long did the call last to New York City? _____

5. How long did the call last to the North Pole? _____

6. What was the total cost of the calls to New York City and Salt Lake City, Utah?

   _____

7. What is the total amount of all the calls? _____

6

PURPLE PRESENTS

On December 3, 1967, Dr. Christiaan Barnard and thirty others performed the first human heart transplant on Louis Washkansky.

Another heart, the Purple Heart, is an award given by the United States Government to any member of the armed forces wounded in action. This decoration is a heart-shaped medal of purple enamel bearing a profile head of George Washington on the front of it.

Match the following items. Place the correct number of the definition by the item.

a. _____ amethyst

b. _____ kingwood

c. _____ purple alfalfa

d. _____ purple vetch

e. _____ purple mica

f. _____ heliotrope plants

g. _____ purple martins

1. shimmering mineral with purple tints

2. plants used as a hillside

3. February's birthstone

4. a violet wood

5. birds

6. light purple flowers that smell like cherry pie

7. plants used to make hay to feed cattle

Can you think of other purple items? List them below.

_____

_____

_____

_____

_____

_____

_____

Below draw a picture of a purple item.

7

95-6

WALT DISNEY

Walt Disney, a famous American cartoonist, was born on December 5, 1901. Mr. Disney was the creator of Disneyland and the well-known characters of Mickey Mouse, Donald Duck, Pluto and countless others. Walt Disney has given hours of enjoyment to both adults and children.

Fill in the information chart on the Walt Disney characters below. The first one is done for you.

CHARACTER	REAL-LIFE ANIMAL OR PERSON	OUTSTANDING FEATURE	PERSONALITY	DESCRIPTIVE ADJECTIVES
Donald Duck	*little white duck*	*funny voice*	*easily angered*	*excitable squawks*
Dumbo				
Mickey Mouse				
Pluto				
Dwarf Grumpy				

Do not do On the back choose one Disney character and write a make-believe adventure involving you and this character.

NUMBERED MEN

The first football game in which the players wore numerals on their uniforms was played on December 5, 1908. The University of Pittsburgh, Pittsburgh, Pennsylvania, had football uniform numbers sewn on the players' uniforms to enable the spectators to easily distinguish the players during the game.

Look at the old-time football snapshots below that were taken from an old scrapbook. Then answer the questions about them.

1. What is the total if you added all the shirt numerals of the football players in the snapshots above? _____

2. What is the total if you added all the shirt numbers of just the middle snapshot players? _____

3. Which players have been given odd numbers on their shirts? _____

4. Which players have been given even shirt numbers? _____

5. What is the total if you eliminate the shirt numbers of the middle picture? _____

6. What is the total if you subtract the right picture player's shirt number from those in the left picture? _____

7. What is the average number using all players' shirts? _____

8. What total would you get if you multiplied all the players' shirts by 3? _____

9. What total would you get if you multiplied the two players' shirts in the left picture by 5? _____

10. What total would you get if you multiplied the player's shirt number on the right by 9 and then divided it by 4? _____

Choose one of the snapshots above and write several sentences describing what is happening in it on the back of this sheet. 9

JOLLY OLD
SAINT NICHOLAS

December 6 is the day that many European countries celebrate as Saint Nicholas Day. Saint Nicholas is a famous bishop in the Roman Catholic Church. It is through his good deeds that the modern day Santa Claus has developed.

Below is an acrostic for the name Santa Claus.

S   is for the *s*nowfall we enjoy more and more.

A   is for *a*ny decoration that we hang upon our door.

N   is for *n*uts cracked for tasty holiday cakes.

T   is for *t*insel placed on ornaments we make.

A   is for the *a*ngels who fly down to enjoy our tree.

C   is for *c*ones resting on green leaves of holly.

L   is for *l*aughter that makes us sound so jolly.

A   is for *a*ll children who wish for clothes or toys.

U   is for *u*s—all the girls and boys.

S   is for the *s*pirit that will fill Christmastime with joy.

Below make up your own acrostic for the name Saint Nicholas.

S

A

I

N

T

N

I

C

H

O

L

A

S

ATTACK!

On Sunday morning *December* 7, 1941, *Pearl Harbor* was quiet until 7 a.m. Then the first *bombs* fell. The *targets* were eight American *battleships* and eighty-four naval vessels *anchored* in the harbor. When all the bombs had stopped falling, the *United States* had eighteen ships sunk or badly damaged, nearly 170 planes *destroyed* and nearly 3,700 casualties.

Because of this attack, President *Franklin Roosevelt* declared war on *Japan* and said that December 7, 1941, would be ''a date which will live in infamy.''

Read the italicized words above and then find them in the puzzle below and circle them.

```
a  b  p  e  a  r  l  h  a  r  b  o  r  e  o  t  n  p
d  w  e  r  v  e  g  g  h  n  o  v  r  i  r  x  m  r
e  m  j  q  e  p  o  d  f  e  m  n  f  n  j  p  t  v
s  c  a  t  e  f  h  e  o  n  b  w  r  t  n  u  m  o
t  x  p  e  y  j  i  c  n  d  s  v  l  r  k  o  t  q
r  w  a  t  a  r  g  e  t  s  s  t  a  t  e  s  m  r
o  l  n  z  e  g  i  m  e  n  r  e  m  o  d  n  e  b
y  d  v  j  z  k  y  b  a  t  t  l  e  s  h  i  p  s
e  e  k  u  n  i  t  e  d  s  t  a  t  e  s  m  t  b
d  t  e  s  m  h  u  r  t  x  o  u  e  s  r  b  e  a
a  n  c  h  o  r  e  d  y  c  t  r  c  r  a  m  e  z
f  r  a  n  k  l  i  n  r  o  o  s  e  v  e  l  t  o
```

On the back of this sheet, put the italicized words in the story above in alphabetical order.

93-4

THE FATHER OF MASS PRODUCTION

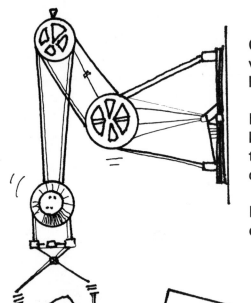

On December 8, 1765, Eli Whitney was born. Eli is known for inventing the cotton gin. This invention made the United States the largest cotton producer in the world.

Eli Whitney also invented a process by which he could make guns by machinery. Before this time, guns were made by hand one at a time. This new process made Eli Whitney the father of mass production.

In order to invent or make something, you must be able to follow directions. See if you can follow these directions.

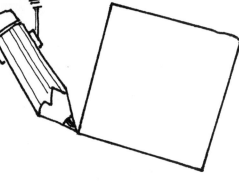

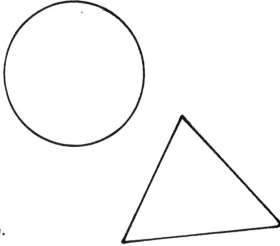

1. Make a line of dots under the square.

2. Print a capital "T" in the circle.

3. Write your name to the left of the triangle.

4. Draw a circle around the diamond.

5. Draw a curved line in the triangle.

6. Draw a line between the circle and square.

7. Put a dot in each section of the X.

8. Draw a square inside the diamond.

9. Write the letter "b" above the circle.

10. Draw a sun inside the square.

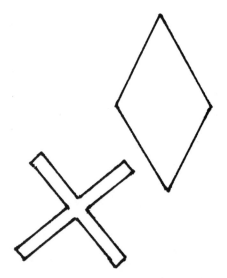

On the back of this sheet, write some directions for a friend to follow.

BALL-BEARING SKATES

On December 9, 1884, the first roller skate, the "ball-bearing" skate, was patented by Levant M. Richardson of Chicago, Illinois. Since then the sport of roller skating has been enjoyed all over the world.

Write prefixes or suffixes on each roller of the skates to make a new word from the root word on the skate shoe. Write the new words on the lines. The first one is done for you.

1. disarm
2. armful
3. unarm

1. _____
2. _____
3. _____

1. _____
2. _____
3. _____

1. _____
2. _____
3. _____

1. _____
2. _____
3. _____

On the back make a list of words describing how you feel when you go roller skating or when you watch someone roller skating.

HOW LONG IS IT?

Have you ever wondered who decided how long a meter should be? On December 10, 1799, the length of a meter was set to equal one ten-millionth of the distance between the equator and the North Pole.

Who set this length? Solve the problems below to find out.

A   Two hundred twenty-two thousand, two hundred twenty-two

B   Seven hundred sixty-six thousand, six hundred sixty-one

C   Two hundred forty-one thousand, nine hundred seventy-six

D   Nine hundred forty-one thousand, two hundred seventy

E   Two hundred forty-one thousand, three hundred twenty-eight

F   Seven hundred eighty-five thousand, four hundred twenty-one

G   Six hundred twenty-two thousand, five hundred fifty-five

H   One hundred twenty-four thousand, seven hundred sixty-nine

I   Two hundred forty-one thousand, three hundred twenty-nine

N   Nine hundred twenty-two thousand, four hundred forty-eight

O   Two hundred forty-two thousand, nine hundred twenty-two

R   Three hundred eighty-two thousand, nine hundred sixty-seven

T   Five hundred twenty-eight thousand, six hundred ninety-seven

U   Five hundred twenty-eight thousand, five hundred ninety-seven

V   Nine hundred twenty-three thousand, five hundred ninety-seven

W   Four hundred thirty-five thousand, six hundred eight

X   Five hundred forty-nine thousand, two hundred sixty-seven

Y   Eight hundred ninety-nine thousand, seven hundred twelve

Z   Nine hundred ninety-nine thousand, nine hundred thirty-two

__528,697__ __124,769__ __241,328__   __785,421__ __382,967__ __241,328__ __922,448__ __241,976__ __124,769__

On the back of this sheet, use the code above and make up a word for a friend to solve.

PEACE AMONG MEN

The first distribution of the Nobel prizes was on December 10, 1901, on the anniversary of the death of Alfred Nobel in 1896. The Nobel Peace Prize is awarded in Oslo, Norway. The other prizes are physics, chemistry, literature, medicine and economics awarded in Stockholm, Sweden.

December 10 is also United Nations Human Rights Day to celebrate the adoption of the 1948 United Nations Declaration of Human Rights.

Two great humanitarians received the Nobel Peace Prize on this day. The Reverend Martin Luther King, Jr. received it in 1964. In 1983, Lech Walesa, the Polish leader for Solidarity, received it on the thirty-fifth anniversary of the United Nations declaration.

As mentioned, one of the Nobel Prizes is a prize for literature. Below is a list of make-believe titles. Choose one and write a story about it. Or make up a title of your own and write about it. Be sure to put the title on the first line.

A Tree with a Halo
Santa's Loudest Complaint
Miracle of the Sleigh Bells
Hitching a Ride with Santa

A Friend in Santa's Stable
The Tree's Treasure
The Christmas Wish I Wish Hadn't Come True

_____

_____

_____

_____

_____

_____

_____

_____

_____

_____

_____

A GROWING NATION

December is the month many states joined the United States. Delaware was the first state to join on December 7, 1787. Pennsylvania became the second state on December 12, 1787; and New Jersey became the third state on December 18, 1787. On December 11, 1816, Indiana became the nineteenth state. A year later Mississippi became the twentieth state on December 10, 1817; and Illinois became the twenty-first state on December 3, 1818. The twenty-second state, Alabama, joined the Union on December 14, 1819. Texas joined on December 29, 1845, as the twenty-eighth state. Iowa, the twenty-ninth state, joined on December 28, 1846.

Choose one of these December states and write a brief report about it on the lines below. You may have to use the back.

Alabama	Illinois	Iowa	New Jersey	Texas
Delaware	Indiana	Mississippi	Pennsylvania	

_____

_____

_____

_____

_____

_____

_____

_____

_____

_____

_____

_____

_____

_____

OUT OF THE DARK!

December 13 is the day for the Swedish celebration of St. Lucia. This festival of light celebrates the return of more daylight hours to the dark winter.

Below are the letters of the alphabet. See how many words pertaining to light you can think of that begin with these letters. Write them on the blanks. The first one is done for you. How bright are you?

A   mperes _____

B _____

C _____

D _____

E _____

F _____

G _____

H _____

I _____

J _____

K _____

L _____

M _____

N _____

O _____

P _____

Q _____

R _____

S _____

T _____

U _____

V _____

W _____

X _____

Y _____

Z _____

17

ARE YOU NUTS?

The first nut and bolt machine was invented by David Wilkinson of Rhode Island. He obtained a patent December 14, 1798.

Look at the nuts and bolts below. Match each nut to the correct bolt problem. Place that letter on the line beside each problem.

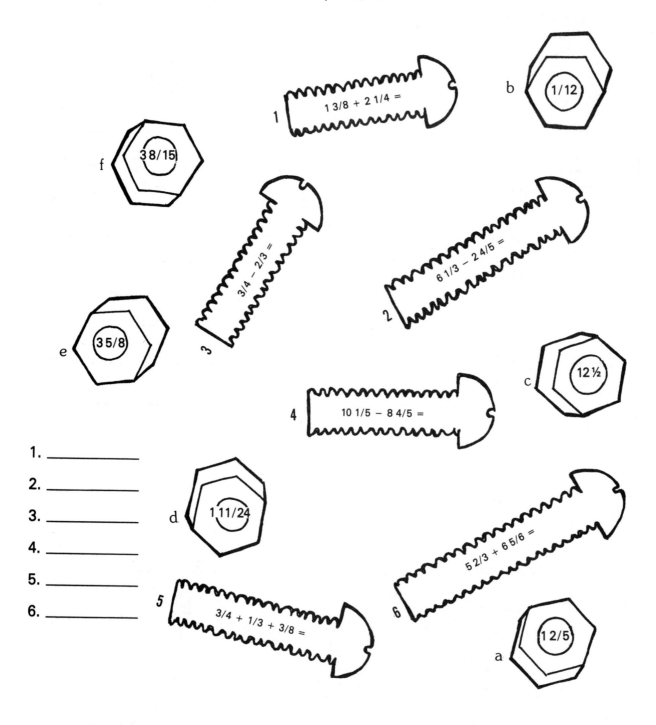

1 3/8 + 2 1/4 =

b 1/12

f 3 8/15

3/4 − 2/3 =

6 1/3 − 2 4/5 =

e 3 5/8

10 1/5 − 8 4/5 =

c 12 ½

d 1 11/24

5 2/3 + 6 5/6 =

3/4 + 1/3 + 3/8 =

a 1 2/5

1. _____
2. _____
3. _____
4. _____
5. _____
6. _____

On the back make up five fraction nut and bolt problems. Give them to a friend to compute.

BRRRRRRR!

On December 14, 1911, the South Pole was discovered by a Norwegian explorer, Roald Amundsen.

The South Pole is covered with ice and snow and is very, very cold. The temperature will fall many degrees below zero.

How cold does it get where you live? Fill in the graph below to show the temperature for the next *five days*. Next, answer the questions below the graph.

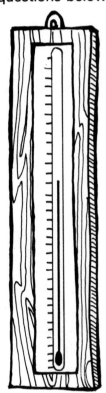

Day					
100					
80					
60					
40					
20					
0					
−20					
−40					

1. Which day had the highest temperature? _____

2. Were there two days that the temperature was the same? _____

   Which days? _____

3. Which day was coldest? _____

4. Which days did the temperature drop below 30°? _____

5. What was the average temperature for the past five days? _____

19

THE FIRST PILOTS

On December 17, 1903, at Kitty Hawk, a lonely spot in North Carolina, two men made the first successful flight in an airplane. On this day they made four flights, the longest lasting fifty-nine seconds at a speed of thirty miles per hour.

Who were these two men who made history? Solve the problems below and then use the code plane to find out who these men were.

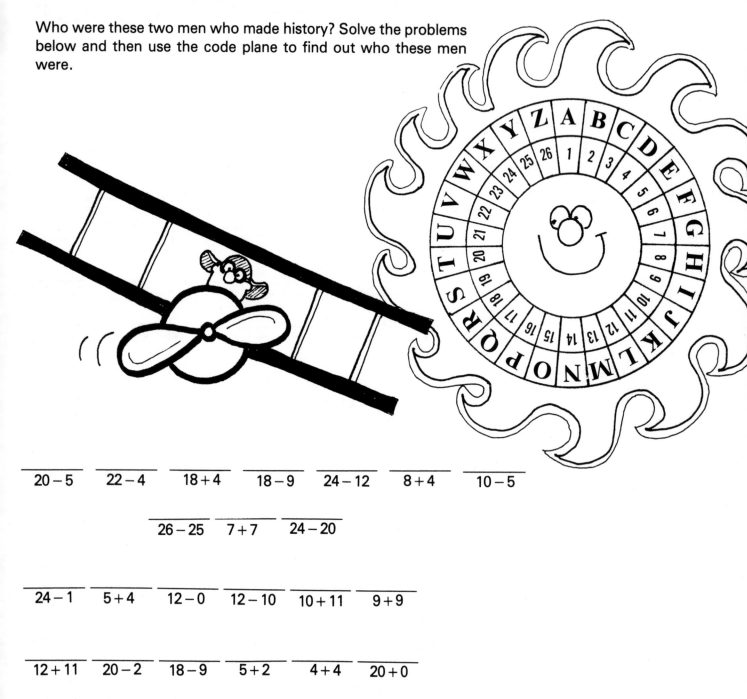

20 − 5	22 − 4	18 + 4	18 − 9	24 − 12	8 + 4	10 − 5

26 − 25	7 + 7	24 − 20

24 − 1	5 + 4	12 − 0	12 − 10	10 + 11	9 + 9

12 + 11	20 − 2	18 − 9	5 + 2	4 + 4	20 + 0

Look up these two famous men in an encyclopedia. On the back write what you found out.

20

THE FIRST THANKSGIVING

The first nationwide, colonial Thanksgiving Day celebration was held Thursday, December 18, 1777, commemorating the surrender of Lieutenant General John Burgoyne. Congress sent this recommendation to set apart a day of thanksgiving to several states, to General Washington and to General Gates.

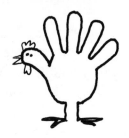

Compute the problems below. Then read the directions and do the puzzle.

1. $85 + 9 =$ _____
2. $98 + 7 =$ _____
3. $119 - 13 =$ _____
4. $78 + 19 =$ _____
5. $99 + 10 =$ _____
6. $90 - 13 =$ _____
7. $92 - 23 =$ _____
8. $75 - 15 =$ _____
9. $13 + 17 =$ _____

10. $35 - 16 =$ _____
11. $114 - 107 =$ _____
12. $42 - 38 =$ _____
13. $21 - 9 =$ _____
14. $96 - 75 =$ _____
15. $15 + 36 =$ _____
16. $89 - 27 =$ _____
17. $56 + 18 =$ _____
18. $93 + 9 =$ _____
19. $100 - 6 =$ _____

20. $38 + 26 =$ _____
21. $93 - 38 =$ _____
22. $16 + 9 =$ _____
23. $19 + 7 =$ _____
24. $72 - 35 =$ _____
25. $29 + 7 =$ _____
26. $17 + 39 =$ _____
27. $27 + 40 =$ _____
28. $150 - 53 =$ _____

29. 105 to $(116 + 9 =$ _____$)$
30. 115 to $(104 + 20 =$ _____$)$
31. 106 to $(119 + 7 =$ _____$)$
32. 116 to $(136 - 9 =$ _____$)$

1. Solve each math problem!

2. Find the first answer. Put your pencil on that dot. Find the second answer. Draw a straight line connecting the two dots.

3. Continue joining each number ANSWER to the one before it until all answers have been connected in SUCCESSION.

4. Then solve the last four problems. Connect these dots.

5. Have fun!

1	2	3	4	5	6	7	8	9	10
11	12	13	14	15	16	17	18	19	20
21	22	23	24	25	26	27	28	29	30
31	32	33	34	35	36	37	38	39	40
41	42	43	44	45	46	47	48	49	50
51	52	53	54	55	56	57	58	59	60
61	62	63	64	65	66	67	68	69	70
71	72	73	74	75	76	77	78	79	80
81	82	83	84	85	86	87	88	89	90
91	92	93	94	95	96	97	98	99	100
101	102	103	104	105	106	107	108	109	110
111	112	113	114	115	116	117	118	119	120
121	122	123	124	125	126	127	128	129	130

On the back make a list of at least fifteen food items you would have had for that celebration in 1777. Alphabetize them.

SU-LIN

On December 18, 1936, the first giant panda arrived in the United States. It was sent as a gift to our country from China. Su-Lin, the gift-bear, weighed only five pounds when it came to San Francisco, California. A panda is known by its shaggy white coat with black markings.

Read the helpful hints and fill in the "black and white" puzzle below.

1. __ __ **B** __ __

2. __ __ __ **L**

3. __ **A** __ __ __ __ __

4. __ __ __ **C** __ __

5. **K** __ __ __

6. __ **A** __ __ __

7. __ **N** __ __ __ __

8. __ **D** __ __ __

9. __ __ **W** __ __ __ __ __

10. **H** __ __ __ __ __ __ __

11. __ __ __ **I** __ __ __

12. __ __ __ **T** __ __ __ __

13. __ __ __ **E** __ __ __ __ __

1. A wild African animal related to the horse, having a light coat with black stripes.
2. A prison where the inmates many times wear black and white striped clothes.
3. A black and white crossing sign to warn drivers about oncoming trains.
4. A black and white ball used in a team sport with 11 men on each team.
5. The moveable black and white parts on a piano. These can be played.
6. A black and white Asian animal that resembles a bear.
7. The black and white clothing a referee wears.
8. Two small white cubes with from one to six black dots on each side.
9. A white paper with black print which is read daily by hundreds of people.
10. A breed of black and white dairy cattle.
11. Small black tiles having from one to six white dots. They are used in a game.
12. The black and white ball used in a game of pool.
13. The first "TV" was black and white.

ONE DOWN, TWO ACROSS

The first crossword puzzle was published on December 21, 1913. It was created by Arthur Wynne and appeared in the supplement of the *New York World* newspaper.

Complete the contraction crossword puzzle below. The apostrophe will take up one square in each word.

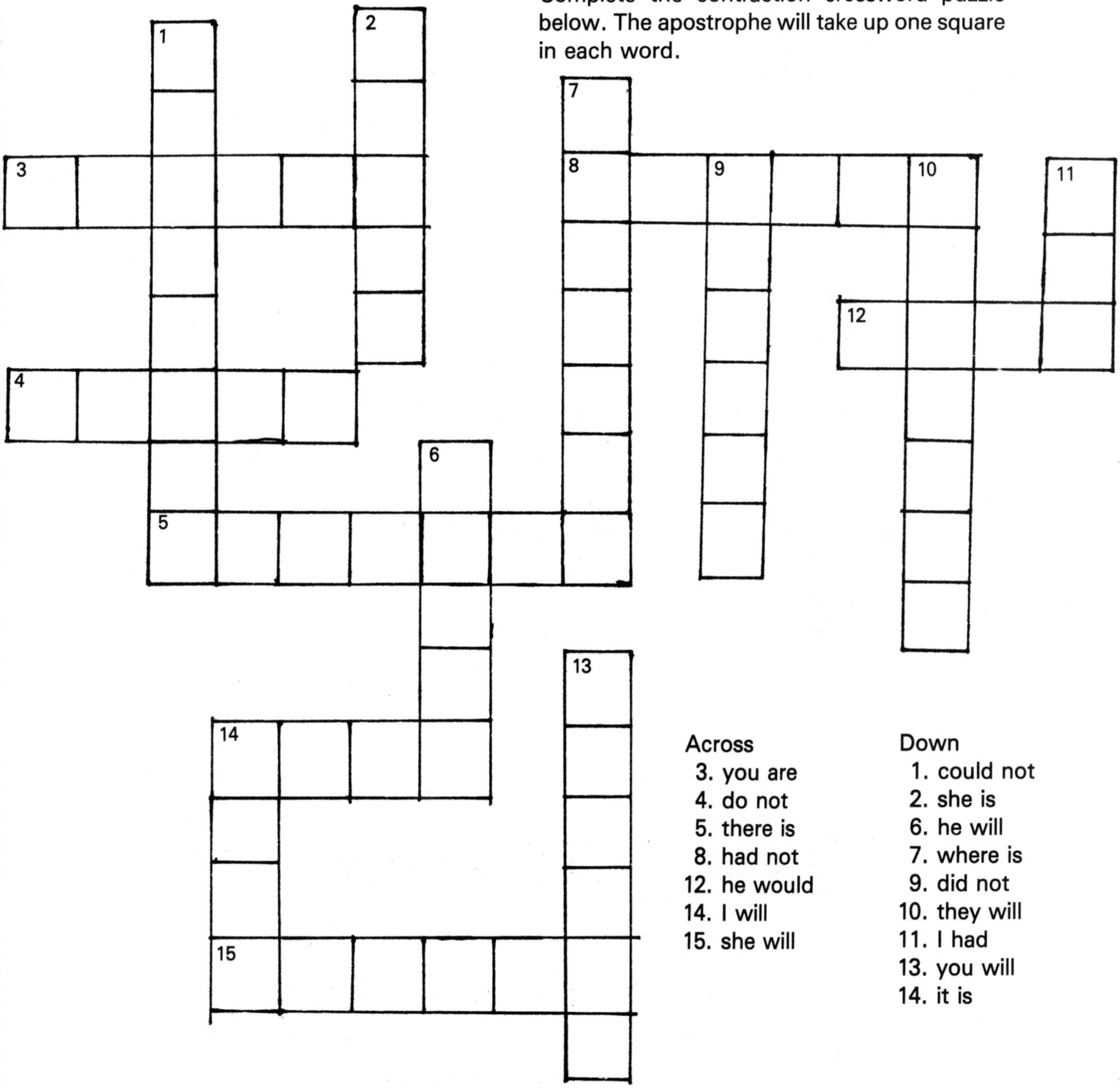

Across
- 3. you are
- 4. do not
- 5. there is
- 8. had not
- 12. he would
- 14. I will
- 15. she will

Down
- 1. could not
- 2. she is
- 6. he will
- 7. where is
- 9. did not
- 10. they will
- 11. I had
- 13. you will
- 14. it is

On the back write sentences using the contractions found in numbers 1 and 10 down and numbers 2, 8 and 12 across.

A NEW HIGHWAY

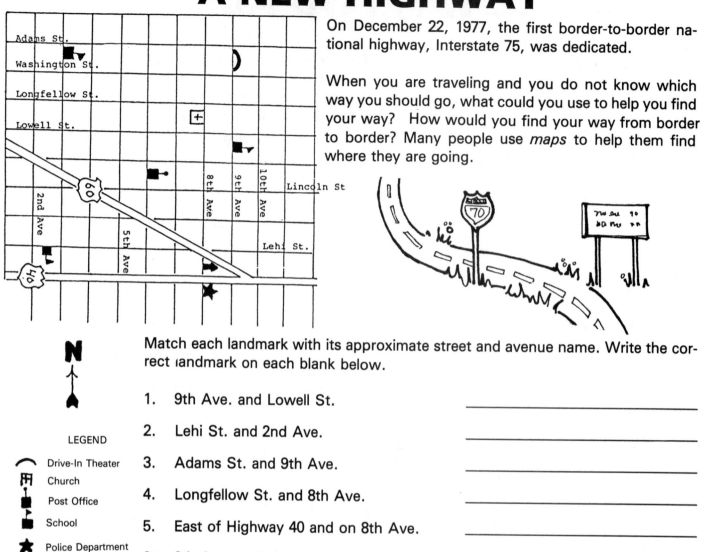

On December 22, 1977, the first border-to-border national highway, Interstate 75, was dedicated.

When you are traveling and you do not know which way you should go, what could you use to help you find your way? How would you find your way from border to border? Many people use *maps* to help them find where they are going.

N
↑

LEGEND

⌒ Drive-In Theater
⊞ Church
◼ Post Office
◼ School
★ Police Department
↑ Courthouse

Match each landmark with its approximate street and avenue name. Write the correct landmark on each blank below.

1. 9th Ave. and Lowell St.

    _____

2. Lehi St. and 2nd Ave.

    _____

3. Adams St. and 9th Ave.

    _____

4. Longfellow St. and 8th Ave.

    _____

5. East of Highway 40 and on 8th Ave.

    _____

6. 6th Ave. and Lincoln St.

    _____

7. Washington St. and 3rd Ave.

    _____

8. Between Highways 40 and 60 just east
    of Lehi St. on 8th Ave.

    _____

On the back draw a map so a friend can find the way to your house.

KIT CARSON

Kit Carson, a famous American *frontiersman,* was born December 24, 1809. He became known as a skillful and daring *hunter, guide* and *soldier.* People who knew Carson said he was *brave, gentle, honest* and wise.

Using the italicized words above, make two words from each word. You may use each letter more than once.

frontiersman   _____   _____

hunter   _____   _____

guide   _____   _____

soldier   _____   _____

brave   _____   _____

gentle   _____   _____

honest   _____   _____

On the back write about an adventure Kit Carson might have had. You may want to use the encyclopedia to discover more facts about him.

SHHHH!

The Christmas song "Silent Night" was written by the schoolteacher Franz Gruber on Christmas Eve, December 24, 1818. It was performed the next day, Christmas Day, in the village church in Oberndorf, Austria.

The following words have at least one silent letter. Circle the silent letter(s) in each.

1. calm
2. bomb
3. thumb
4. comb
5. dumb
6. balm
7. climb
8. limb
9. limbs
10. glisten
11. listen
12. sigh
13. sighs
14. sighing
15. soften
16. debt
17. debtor
18. hasten
19. hastens

20. doubt
21. though
22. although
23. thought
24. dough
25. fasten
26. fastens
27. salmon
28. often
29. almond
30. moisten
31. crumb
32. crumbs
33. numb
34. lamb
35. lambs
36. lambskin
37. right
38. mighty

RED LINGO!

Besides being Christmas, December 25 is Clara Barton's birth-day. She was born in 1821 and was a great help to the wounded during the Civil War. She is best remembered for starting the American Red Cross. She became the first president of the American Red Cross in 1881.

Are you "reddy" to know more about reds? Below is a list of reds and a list of definitions. Match them by placing the letter of the definition by the correct word.

1. _____ red drum   a. rules that cause delay

2. _____ redcap   b. a bird

3. _____ red hot   c. a spider

4. _____ red-letter day   d. a fish

5. _____ red root   e. a Sioux Indian chief

6. _____ Red Cloud   f. a porter

7. _____ red gum   g. a plant

8. _____ red mite   h. a tree

9. _____ red-eyed vireo   i. a poisonous snake

10. _____ red adder   j. a happy day

11. _____ red tape   k. very angry; or candy

What other "red" words can you think of? List them below.

DON'T BE SNOWED

On December 26, 1947, the northeastern section of our nation had one of the worst blizzards in recorded history. Twenty-eight and eight-tenths inches of snow fell in New York City.

Don't let this math "snow" you. Complete each snowflake by writing all the names for each numeral placed inside the snowflake. The first one is done for you.

On the back write a word bank of words you think of when you hear the word "snow." Put at least twelve words in your list.

LOUIS PASTEUR

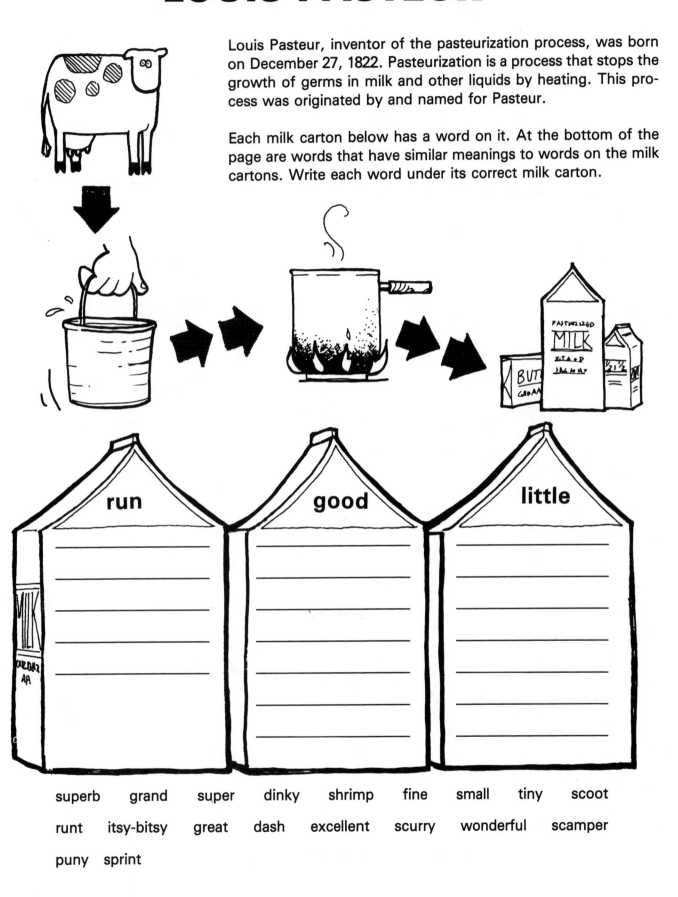

Louis Pasteur, inventor of the pasteurization process, was born on December 27, 1822. Pasteurization is a process that stops the growth of germs in milk and other liquids by heating. This process was originated by and named for Pasteur.

Each milk carton below has a word on it. At the bottom of the page are words that have similar meanings to words on the milk cartons. Write each word under its correct milk carton.

run   **good**   **little**

superb   grand   super   dinky   shrimp   fine   small   tiny   scoot

runt   itsy-bitsy   great   dash   excellent   scurry   wonderful   scamper

puny   sprint

GUM ANYONE?

A patent for the first chewing gum was issued on December 28, 1869, to William Semple of Mount Vernon, Ohio. Chewing gum is a confection that is chewed but not swallowed. People in most countries chew gum because they like the taste. Today chewing gum is produced by more than five hundred companies in over ninety countries.

Read the words in the gum wrappers below. Record the number of syllables in each word. Then rewrite the word drawing a slash between each syllable. The first one is done for you.

1. ornament   __3__   or/na/ment _____

2. supervise   _____   _____

3. comprehension   _____   _____

4. refrain   _____   _____

5. independence   _____   _____

6. perfection   _____   _____

7. commotion   _____   _____

8. superhuman   _____   _____

9. edible   _____   _____

10. immigrate   _____   _____

11. inexpensive   _____   _____

12. magnificence   _____   _____

13. bedraggle   _____   _____

14. additive   _____   _____

15. bisect   _____   _____

On the back put the above words in alphabetical order.

JANUARY

Winter makes me think of marshmallows,
Yummy and chewy,
Vanilla ice cream, cold and white,
Clouds that are fluffy,
And just seem to glide away.
But what I have to do . . .
  is SHOVEL!

Kevin
Age 6

From *Fragile as Butterflies* © Good Apple, Inc., 1983

January

Sunday	Monday	Tuesday	Wednesday	Thursday	Friday	Saturday

A. Run off enough calendars on the opposite page so that each student can have one of his own. You may also want to reproduce the cutouts found at the bottom of this page. The student can use these cutouts as "stickers" for his calendar. If one side of the pattern is put on the fold and the rest is cut out, the student can lift the pattern and write on the inside. These cutout "stickers" can be decorated as the student wishes. The cutout can be taped or glued to the appropriate place on the calendar.

The following activities are suggested uses for the calendar:

1. Each student can make an attractive cover for spelling assignments on the back of his calendar. He can write the word "Spelling" and his name using "skis" and/or things to do with skiing. When the cover is attached to the assignments, the calendar will be on the inside. The student can put a cutout on the days he has finished an assignment.
2. Each student can put a sticker on the calendar for each day he has kept one of his New Year Resolutions. (Hint: You may have to explain making resolutions.)

B. Enlarge the calendar (on the opposite page) to design a bulletin board for your classroom. An example is shown above. You may want students to complete ongoing activities to fill in the calendar. One student can be assigned to a specific day of the month. Some suggestions are given below. Enlarge the cutout patterns for students to write down the information they wish to place on the calendar. If one side of the pattern is put on the fold and the rest is cut out, the student can lift the pattern and write on the inside. These cutout stickers can be decorated as the student wishes. The cutout can be taped or glued to the appropriate place on the calendar.

1. Have a different student record the temperature, the wind-chill factor and the resulting temperature for each day. Wind-chill indices can be found in encyclopedias.
2. Have students brainstorm tips for keeping warm. Then have them write one of these tips for each day on the calendar.
3. Each day have a different student draw a unique snowflake on the calendar.

 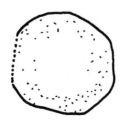  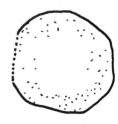 

ACTIVITIES FOR JANUARY

THE FLAG MAKER

Betsy Ross was born on January 1. It is said that the first flag made by Betsy Ross (Elizabeth Griscom Ross) in her little shop in Philadelphia, Pennsylvania, was done at the request of George Washington for the Continental Congress.

Read the puzzle below. Color in all words having the long $\bar{a}$ sound anywhere in the word. Look carefully and it will tell you the year in which Betsy Ross was born.

enabled	prey	reign	labor	graven	plague	agent	wavy	nature	sacred
chaste	stray	argue	graces	fade	wrath	area	available	stalk	detail
claimed	castes	oval	vapor	invade	mass	damper	gazelle	square	agency
related	alas	apply	wager	quake	estate	radar	because	trails	talk
mosaic	alloy	balm	ranges	varied	cloak	acre	spray	above	death
create	access	total	avail	years	caring	basis	rates	knack	unfair
retained	axis	plaza	raged	changes	stray	painful	stated	nation	paid

The Continental Congress met in the year 1777. Knowing this, figure out how old Betsy Ross was when she made the first flag.

Betsy Ross was _____ years old on her birthday in 1777.

On the back choose five words which you have shaded in from the puzzle above and make a sentence using each word correctly.

35

A "HOLEY" PRESENT

The first cheese factory cooperative was established by farmers in Cheshire, Massachusetts. They pressed a cheese at the farm of Elisha Brown which weighed 1,235 pounds. It was placed on a wagon drawn by six horses and presented to President Thomas Jefferson at The White House on January 1, 1802.

Read the sentences below. Each sentence has a "hole" in it due to a missing word. Read the part of speech below the "hole" and write in a correct word of that kind.

1. Bill made the cheese, but _____
   _____pronoun_____
   didn't get to taste it.

2. It was a _____ day
   _____adjective_____
   when they delivered the cheese.

3. The horses _____ pulled
   _____adverb_____
   the wagon down the dusty road.

4. "How will we transport this _____
   _____adjective_____
   cheese?" he cried.

5. They decided to put it on a long _____.
   _____noun_____

6. The horses _____ and
   _____verb_____
   _____, but they couldn't
   _____verb_____
   move the immense cheese.

7. President Jefferson had a _____
   _____adjective_____
   look on his face.

Many people say "cheese" when they smile for a photograph. Below are some words you could use instead. Pronounce these words and you will smile, smile, smile.

EASY	HARD
alleys	aborigines
babies	diaries
cherries	galaxies
fleas	possibilities
honeybees	universities
monkeys	warranties

Now make up some of your own. Write your smile words on the lines below.

_____

_____

_____

_____

_____

_____

_____

_____

36

COLOR MY WORLD

The words on the large crayon:

crimson
sapphire
topaz
emerald
sepia
orchid
ebony
henna
vermillion
persimmon
cobalt
mauve
licorice
mahogany
scarlet
azure
maize
pistachio
magenta
charcoal
chartreuse

The first "ink paste" was invented by Frank Buckley Cooney of Minneapolis, Minnesota, on January 1, 1924. He sold the right to manufacture the ink paste to the American Crayon Company. Since then crayons (ink paste) are used across our country daily.

Read the color words on the large crayon. Then write them on the given lines under the correct color heading.

Green

1. _____

2. _____

3. _____

Red

1. _____

2. _____

3. _____

4. _____

5. _____

6. _____

Black

1. _____

2. _____

3. _____

Brown

1. _____

2. _____

3. _____

Blue

1. _____

2. _____

3. _____

Purple

1. _____

2. _____

Yellow

1. _____

37

A HOCKEY HAPPENING!

Six states were admitted to the United States during January. Georgia became the fourth state on January 2, 1788, while Connecticut became the fifth one January 9 that same year. The twenty-sixth state to join was Michigan on January 26, 1837. On January 29, 1861, Kansas became the thirty-fourth state. Utah was admitted as the forty-fifth state on January 4, 1896. New Mexico, the forty-seventh state, joined January 6, 1912.

January is also the time that many hockey games are played. Most of these games determine the league leaders. Below are listed some of the hockey teams. Circle the two teams that come from a state that was admitted in January.

Boston Bruins
Buffalo Sabres
California Golden Seals
Chicago Black Hawks
Detroit Red Wings
Hartford Whalers

Los Angeles Kings
Minnesota North Stars
Montreal Canadiens
New York Islanders
New York Rangers

Philadelphia Flyers
Pittsburgh Penguins
St. Louis Blues
Toronto Maple Leafs
Vancouver Canucks

If you owned a hockey team, what would you name it? _____

Where would your arena be located? _____

Which of the teams above is closest to your community? _____

_____

Which of the teams is farthest from your community? _____

_____

WHITE "PUZZLERS"

Alaska, the forty-ninth state, was admitted to the United States on January 3, 1959. Alaska is our largest state with 586,400 square miles. Nearly a third of Alaska lies within the Arctic Circle. Many of the animals that live in Alaska have white fur. These include the polar bear, Arctic hare, and Alaskan huskie.

Below are some "white puzzlers." First answer each question with a "yes" or "no." Then explain your answer. Write your answer on the blanks provided.

1. Are whitecaps worn on the head? _____

   _____

2. Are whiteheads blond children? _____

   _____

3. Are whiteners used to bleach clothing? _____

   _____

4. Does white heat mean slightly hot? _____

   _____

5. Is a white feather a symbol of bravery? _____

   _____

6. Can cars have whitewalls? _____

   _____

7. Are toys sold at a "white sale"? _____

   _____

8. Are animals sold at a "white elephant" sale? _____

   _____

HAPPY BIRTHDAY, JAKOB GRIMM

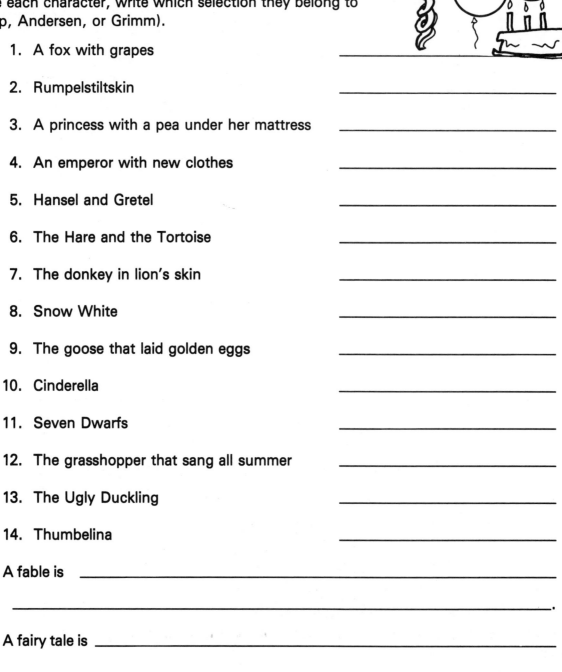

January 4, 1785, is the birthday of Jakob Grimm. He and his brother Wilhelm are coauthors of *Grimm's Fairy Tales.* They went around their native country and wrote down the popular stories and published them.

To honor Jakob, a surprise party has been planned. Characters from the fairy tales have been invited. However, some of the characters from Aesop's Fables and Hans Christian Andersen's fairy tales have slipped in. On the blank line beside each character, write which selection they belong to (Aesop, Andersen, or Grimm).

1. A fox with grapes _____

2. Rumpelstiltskin _____

3. A princess with a pea under her mattress _____

4. An emperor with new clothes _____

5. Hansel and Gretel _____

6. The Hare and the Tortoise _____

7. The donkey in lion's skin _____

8. Snow White _____

9. The goose that laid golden eggs _____

10. Cinderella _____

11. Seven Dwarfs _____

12. The grasshopper that sang all summer _____

13. The Ugly Duckling _____

14. Thumbelina _____

A fable is _____

_____.

A fairy tale is _____

_____.

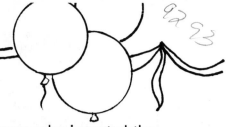

A BIRTHDAY

Louis Braille, born on January 4, 1809, was a blind Frenchman who invented the Braille system of printing and writing for the blind. The system uses raised points or dots on paper for letters.

Look at the Braille alphabet below and spell out *Louis Braille* using the Braille alphabet.

A B C D E F G H I J

K L M N O P Q R S T

U V X Y Z W

L ___ ___ ___ ___ ___

___ ___ ___ ___ ___ ___ ___

THIS IS HARD TO DO...

On the back of this sheet, make up a word for a friend to solve using the Braille alphabet.

THE PEANUT SPECIALIST

On January 5, 1943, George Washington Carver died. This man invented peanut butter and over three hundred other things that could be made from a peanut.

Use only the words on the peanuts and make as many different sentences as possible. You may have to use the back.

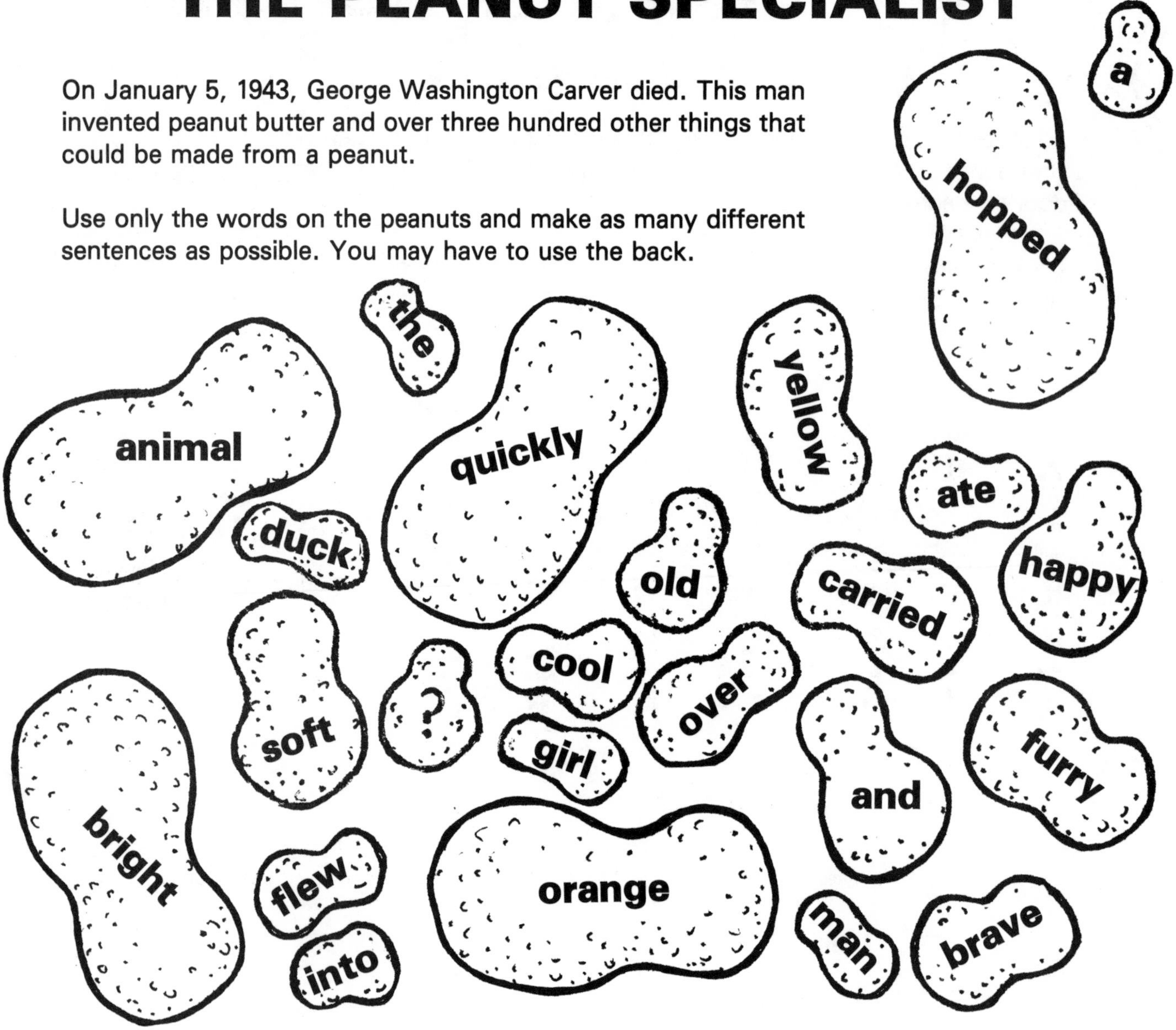

a

hopped

the

yellow

animal

quickly

ate

happy

duck

old

carried

cool

over

soft

?

girl

and

furry

bright

flew

orange

man

brave

into

_____

_____

_____

_____

_____

_____

On the back of this sheet, make up five words using the letters in the word "peanut." (You may use the letters more than once.)

THINK BIG AND ADD TWO!

Galileo discovered the moons of Jupiter on January 7, 1610. Jupiter is the largest of the planets in the solar system. Some of the "largest" on our planet Earth are listed below. The last two letters have been omitted. Add them.

1. The largest continent is Euras ____ ____.

2. The largest ocean is Pacif ____ ____.

3. The largest gulf is Gulf of Mexi ____ ____.

4. The largest living creature is the blue wha____ ____

5. The largest bird is the North African ostri____ ____

Can you find the largest of the following? Write the answers in the blanks.

6. The tallest animal is the _____.

7. The largest primate is the _____.

8. The largest marsupial is the _____.

9. The largest reptile was the _____.

10. The largest amphibian is the _____.

11. The longest snakes are the _____.

Make up some of your own "the largest is." They can be silly or serious. Have fun! Write them below.

9293

THE KING OF ROCK 'N' ROLL

Have you ever heard of the "King of Rock 'n' Roll"? Do you know who it is? Elvis Presley, known as the King, was born on January 8, 1935. His music became very popular. Even today you can hear his music on the radio.

Press two buttons on the jukebox below to make a compound word for each sentence. Write the words on the lines.

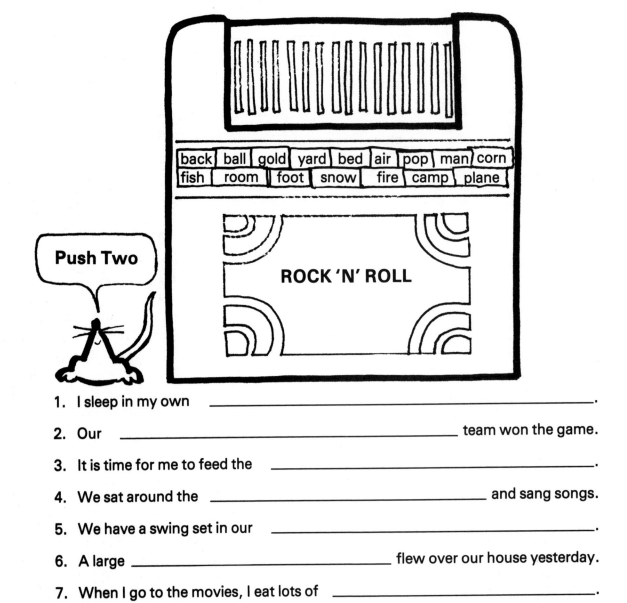

| back | ball | gold | yard | bed | air | pop | man | corn |
| fish | room | foot | snow | fire | camp | plane |

Push Two

ROCK 'N' ROLL

1. I sleep in my own _____.

2. Our _____ team won the game.

3. It is time for me to feed the _____.

4. We sat around the _____ and sang songs.

5. We have a swing set in our _____.

6. A large _____ flew over our house yesterday.

7. When I go to the movies, I eat lots of _____.

8. Every winter I build a _____.

On the back of this sheet, use three of the compound words in a sentence.

44

A PRESIDENTIAL FLIGHT

On January 9, 1793, at 10:16 a.m., Jean Blanchard of France made the first balloon flight in which a Presidential order was carried. He left Philadelphia, Pennsylvania, and made a forty-minute flight landing in Gloucester County, New Jersey, about fifteen miles away.

Read and compute the problems in each balloon below. Put the various operation signs found at the top of each balloon into the box to make three different problems. Then place your answers on the lines provided. (Compute the problems on scratch paper or on the back.)

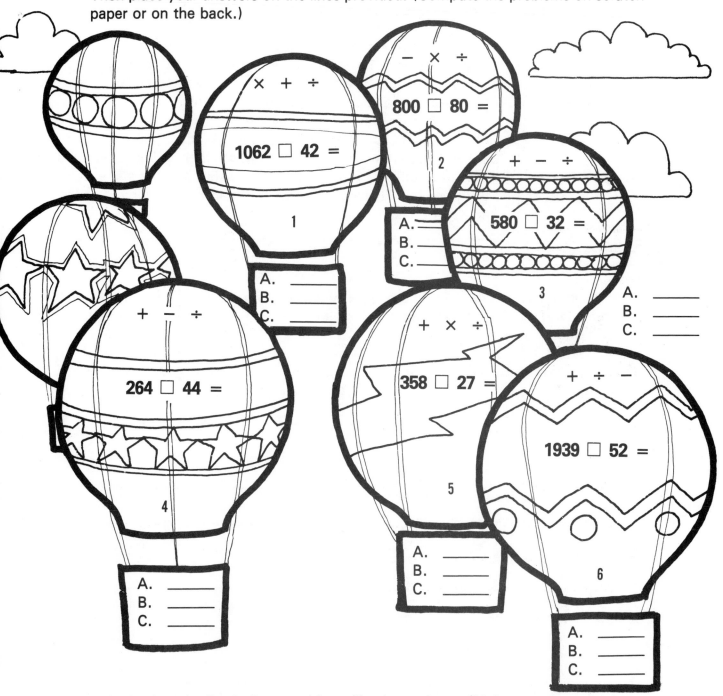

1. × + ÷
   1062 □ 42 =
   A. ____
   B. ____
   C. ____

2. − × ÷
   800 □ 80 =
   A. ____
   B. ____
   C. ____

3. + − ÷
   580 □ 32 =
   A. ____
   B. ____
   C. ____

4. + − ÷
   264 □ 44 =
   A. ____
   B. ____
   C. ____

5. + × ÷
   358 □ 27 =
   A. ____
   B. ____
   C. ____

6. + ÷ −
   1939 □ 52 =
   A. ____
   B. ____
   C. ____

On the back make five balloon problems like those above. (Make sure the operation signs fit the problems.)

45

THE SEEING EYE

The Seeing Eye, a nonprofit association whose purpose is to train dogs to guide blind people, was incorporated on January 9, 1920. "Buddy" was the first Seeing Eye dog used to guide a blind person. This dog was brought over from Vevey, Switzerland.

RALPH

GUIDE DOGS

A guide dog is a specially trained dog used to guide blind people. These dogs must be smart, physically fit and responsible. German shepherds, Labrador retrievers, golden retrievers and boxers are some of the best kinds of dogs for helping the blind.

The dogs go to school for three to five months. Each dog must get used to the leather harness it will wear when guiding the blind. It learns to watch for traffic, cross streets safely and sometimes follow a zigzag course. These dogs learn commands like "forward," "left," "right," and "sit."

Read the information above. Fill in the blanks with the correct words. Then put the numbered letters in the boxes below. If you do it correctly, it will tell you what breed of dog "Buddy" was.

1. A dog trained to help blind people is called a __ __ __ __ __ dog.
                                              12   9 4

2. These dogs must be smart and __ __ __ __ __ __ __ __ __ __ fit.
                                   5 3

3. They go to school for three to five __ __ __ __ __ __.
                                        11   6

4. Guide dogs must get used to wearing a leather __ __ __ __ __ __ __.
                                                         8 7 2

5. These dogs learn to watch for __ __ __ __ __ __ __ when crossing the street.
                                  1

6. Guide dogs also learn to listen to verbal __ __ __ __ __ __ __ __.
                                                               10

1	2	3	4	5	6	7	8	9	10	11	12

On the back write five situations in which a blind person would need the help of a guide dog.

46

91-92

"DEAR ABBY"

The first "Dear Abby" advice column appeared on January 9, 1956. People write to "Dear Abby" to ask her advice on various problems they are having. Their letters and her answers appear together in the paper. Usually real names are not printed to protect the letter writer.

Below is a letter to "Dear Abby." Read it and then answer the letter as if you were Abby. Write your answer in the blanks provided.

Dear Abby,
    I am a sixth-grade student going to junior high in a new town. We moved from a small town, and I left all my friends. I'm kind of shy and can't meet new people very easy. I don't know what to do to make new friends. We lived in the other place all my life. Please help!

                        Lonely

Dear Lonely, _____

_____

_____

_____

_____

_____

_____

_____

_____

_____

_____

47

"BLACK GOLD"

The great oil industry in the state of Texas began on January 10, 1901, with the discovery of the Spindletop Oil Field near Beaumont, Texas. Many people have become wealthy because of the discovery of this wonderful "black gold."

The oil rigs below have money spurting out from each of them. Compute the total amount coming out of each well and write this answer in the box at the bottom of each rig. Be careful with the decimals.

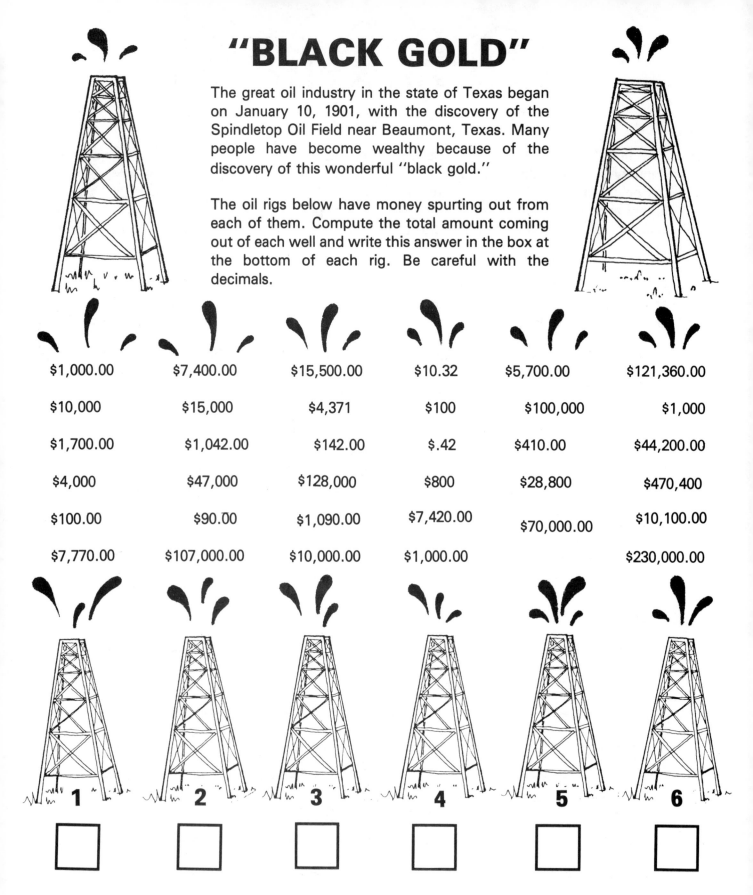

1	2	3	4	5	6
$1,000.00	$7,400.00	$15,500.00	$10.32	$5,700.00	$121,360.00
$10,000	$15,000	$4,371	$100	$100,000	$1,000
$1,700.00	$1,042.00	$142.00	$.42	$410.00	$44,200.00
$4,000	$47,000	$128,000	$800	$28,800	$470,400
$100.00	$90.00	$1,090.00	$7,420.00	$70,000.00	$10,100.00
$7,770.00	$107,000.00	$10,000.00	$1,000.00		$230,000.00

On the back make four oil wells with money spurting out of them. Give these problems to a friend to do. Then check his/her answers.

48

A FOLK COMPOSER

January 13 is celebrated as Stephen Foster Memorial Day. It was on this day in 1864 that the great black American composer died. Mr. Foster wrote some of America's best loved folk songs. Altogether he wrote about two hundred songs. Some of the most famous are "My Old Kentucky Home, Good Night," "Swanee River," "Oh! Susanna," "Camptown Races," and "Jeanie with the Light Brown Hair."

Folk music is music that is handed down generation by generation. It is usually about everyday life, often telling a story. Look up some folk songs and read them. Then on the blanks below, write your own folk song. Good luck!

_____

_____

_____

_____

_____

_____

_____

_____

_____

_____

_____

_____

_____

_____

_____

_____

MARTIN

I HAVE A DREAM

Martin Luther King, Jr., was born on January 15, 1929. This date was called Human Relations Day but now is a national holiday in honor of his birthday. Martin Luther King, Jr., is very famous for his many speeches and marches for Civil Rights. He led many activities for change without violence.

See if you can find any of Mr. King's speeches or famous sayings. Write some of the most impressive ones on the lines below.

How would you celebrate this new holiday? Below design a banner, birthday card, or any other souvenir in honor of his birthday. You may want to include how old he would be if he had lived.

A JACK-OF-ALL-TRADES

Benjamin *Franklin* was born in Boston, Massachusetts, on *January* 17, 1706. He was the fifteenth child and *youngest* son in a *family* of seventeen children. *Benjamin* was a jack-of-all-trades. During his life he *concerned* himself with such things as statesmanship, soapmaking, book *printing* and cabbage growing. He also invented an *efficient* heating stove and proved that *lightning* was *electricity*.

Look at the story above and write the italicized words in the word column and then fill out the other columns as indicated.

Italicized Word	Divide into Syllables	Number of Syllables
Franklin	Frank-lin	2

On the back of this sheet, put the italicized words in alphabetical order.

ICE CREAM, PLEASE

The ice cream rolling machine was invented by Carl Rutherford Taylor of Cleveland, Ohio, who obtained patent number 1,481,813 on January 19, 1924. The patent was for a "machine for spinning or turning a waffle."

Write the homonym on the scoop of ice cream that matches each word on the cone. The first one is done for you.

FORWARD AND BACKWARD!

...and if you elect me president

January 20 is the date for the Presidential inauguration. This is held every four years in our nation's capital. It is a time for looking forwards and backwards. We can look back on the past four years' events and look forward to an even better new four years. Below are some words that are spelled exactly the same forward or backwards. See how many more you can think of. List them; then try the riddles.

bib	did	dud	nun	tat
pep	pup	tot	eve	eye

_____

_____

_____

1. What is an article of clothing for babies? _____

2. What word means "the night"? _____

3. What is a kind of communication for the navy? _____

4. What word means a young canine? _____

5. What word is the sound of a horn? _____

6. What word means a small child? _____

7. What sound do young birds make? _____

9293

A FAMOUS SUB

On January 21, 1954, the first atomic submarine was launched. It was christened by President Eisenhower's wife, Mamie, in Gordon, Connecticut. What was the name of this famous submarine?

Solve the problems below. Write the sum under the correct line and then match the sum with its matching letter. Write the letter on the line. The first one is done for you.

A	B	D	G	I	J	L	N	O	R	S	T	U	V
163	164	110	73	109	111	168	83	165	241	173	114	240	177

1. 28
    31
    +24
    ———
    83

2. 14
    92
    +57
    ———

3. 82
    68
    +90
    ———

4. 26
    37
    +51
    ———

5. 45
    49
    +15
    ———

6. 53
    82
    +33
    ———

7. 90
    80
    +70
    ———

8. 101
    22
    +50
    ———

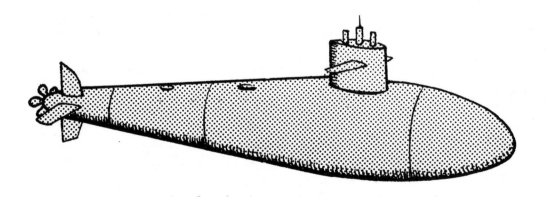

1 N 2 ___ 3 ___ 4 ___ 5 ___ 6 ___ 7 ___ 8 ___
 83

A BULL'S-EYE

The first National Archery Association was formed January 23, 1879, in Crawfordsville, Indiana, by representatives of eight archery clubs.

Read the prefixes on the target below. Then do the activities.

Hit the bull's-eye with the arrows. Match the correct letters on the arrows to the correct prefixes in the target. Write the letters in the blanks.

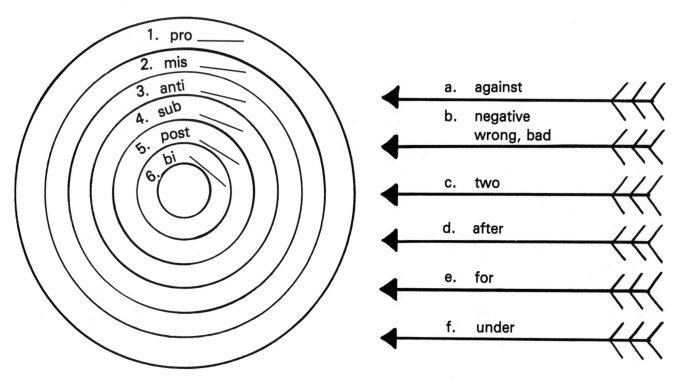

1. pro _____
2. mis _____
3. anti _____
4. sub _____
5. post _____
6. bi _____

a. against

b. negative wrong, bad

c. two

d. after

e. for

f. under

Now see if you can define the words below. Use your knowledge from the target practice. Write the meanings on the lines.

1. antislavery _____

2. subway _____

3. bimonthly _____

4. misconduct _____

5. pronoun _____

6. postpone _____

THE GOLD RUSH IS ON

On January 24, 1848, James Marshall discovered gold at Sutter's Mill in California.

Read the map shown here. Then write three different directions on how to get to Sutter's Mill by starting at the three different points on the map and following the path marked.

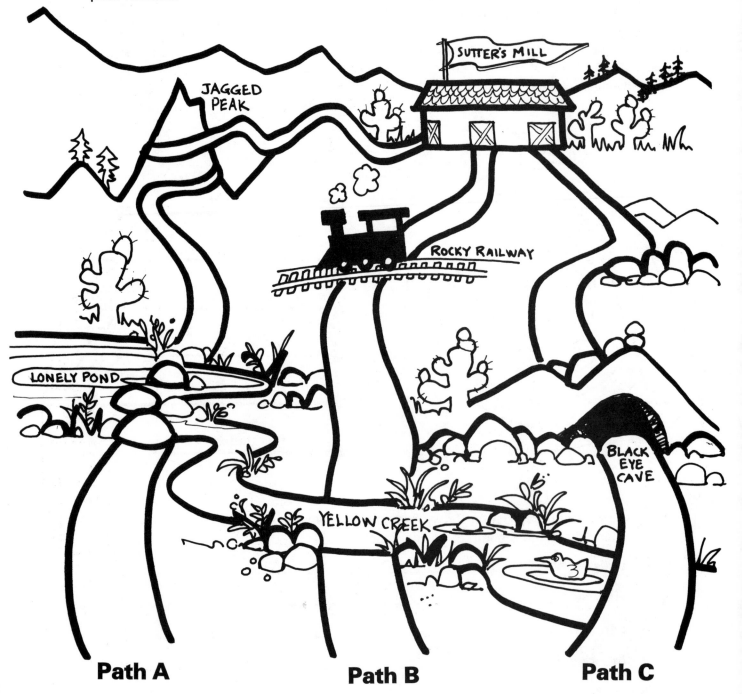

On the back of this sheet, write down five things you would buy if you had one hundred pounds of gold.

GO NELLIE GO!

On January 25, 1890, journalist Nellie Bly broke the record for going around the world in eighty days. She made it in seventy-two days, six hours and eleven minutes.

Help Nellie around the world. Solve the problems all the way around the world. Start with "7." Write the answer in the box after each problem. If your last answer is "80," you helped Nellie make it around the world.

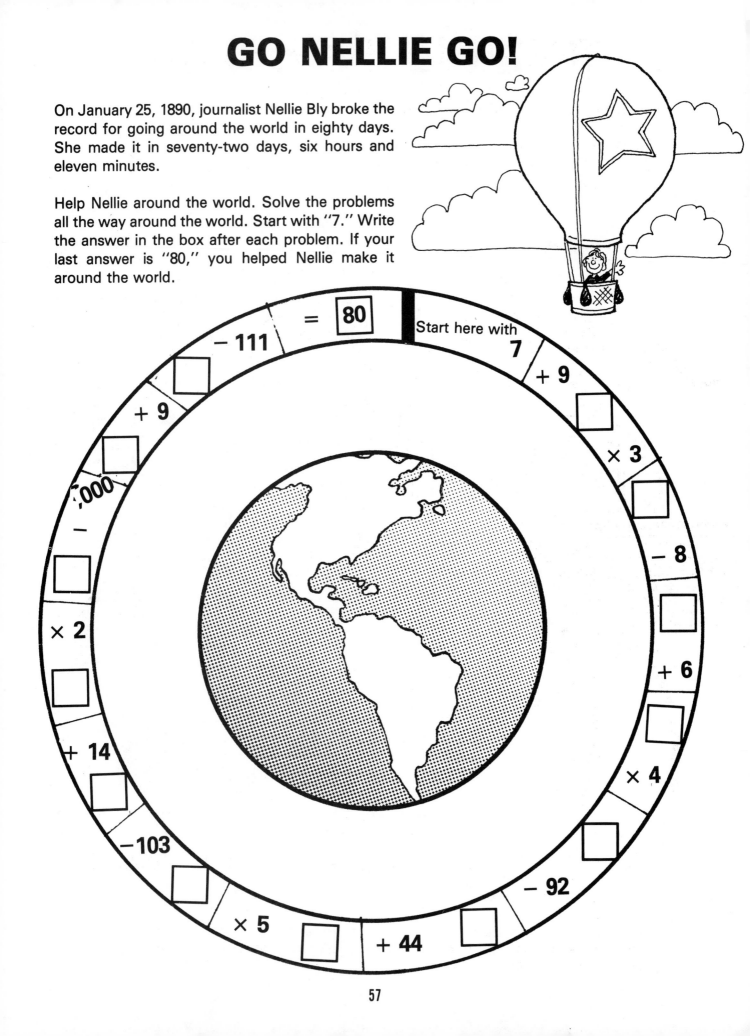

Start here with
7

$+ 9$

$\times 3$

$- 8$

$+ 6$

$\times 4$

$- 92$

$+ 44$

$\times 5$

$- 103$

$+ 14$

$\times 2$

$- \_,000$

$+ 9$

$- 111$

$= \boxed{80}$

92-93

THE COAST GUARD

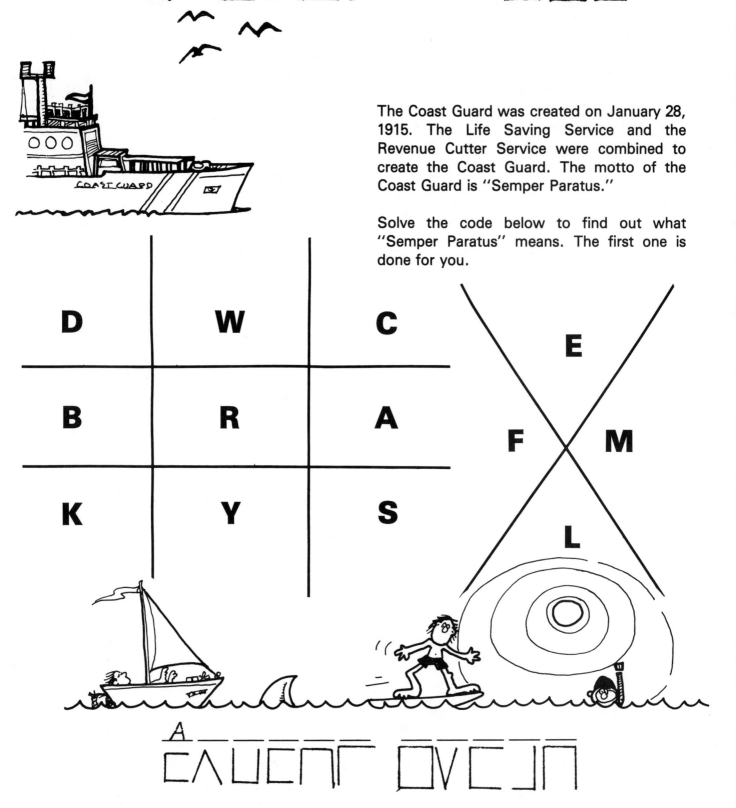

The Coast Guard was created on January 28, 1915. The Life Saving Service and the Revenue Cutter Service were combined to create the Coast Guard. The motto of the Coast Guard is "Semper Paratus."

Solve the code below to find out what "Semper Paratus" means. The first one is done for you.

D	W	C
B	R	A
K	Y	S

E

F   M

L

A _ _ _ _ _   _ _ _ _ _

On the back of this sheet, make up a word for a friend to solve using the code above.

58

GOING TO THE TOP!

The first ski tow (rope) was built by Robert Royce and placed in operation January 28, 1934, at Woodstock, Vermont. About 900 yards of manila rope were spliced together, passed over pulleys and around a wheel, attached to a tractor and went up the hill about 300 yards.

Read the abbreviations for skiing conditions below. Then read and answer the questions.

SNOW CONDITIONS CHART	
PO = powder snow	HP = hard packed snow
NS = new snow	GR = granular snow
IC = icy conditions	HB = hard base
WC = wet conditions	SB = soft base
BS = bare spots	DC = dangerous conditions

Write the meanings of the skiing conditions messages given below. NOTE: The numerals represent inches of snow.

1. Northwest slopes IC. Base 54 HP. South slope DC.

   _____

   _____

2. Waiting time for the lifts. 4 NS over 5-50 HB. All trails are excellent. Watch IC and WC on roads.

   _____

   _____

3. Skiing poor with lift not operating. North trail has 6 PO on 10 HP, 4 PO on 7 HP in low areas. BS on south slope.

   _____

   _____

Use the abbreviation chart above to write a skiing condition message telling a skier the following information:

4. The north slope has 2-5 inches of powdered snow. Snow has soft base. Roads have icy conditions. No lifts operating.

   _____

   _____

THE AMERICAN BASEBALL LEAGUE

The American Baseball League was organized on January 29, 1900, in Philadelphia, Pennsylvania. It originally consisted of eight teams: Buffalo, Chicago, Cleveland, Detroit, Indianapolis, Kansas City, Milwaukee and Minneapolis.

Look at the baseball formula below to find out each player's batting average. Compute the problems below using the formula, and place the answers on the baseball diamond lines.

# of hits ÷ # of times at bat × 1000 = batting average

Player	# of hits	# of times at bat
1. Player #1	15	60
2. Player #2	10	60
3. Player #3	30	87
4. Player #4	4	50
5. Player #5	20	70
6. Player #6	52	150
7. Player #7	35	99
8. Player #8	60	200
9. Player #9	55	135

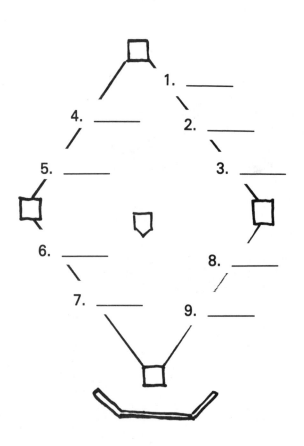

1. _____
2. _____
3. _____
4. _____
5. _____
6. _____
7. _____
8. _____
9. _____

10. Who had the best batting average? _____

11. What is the overall batting average of players #1, #2, #3, #4, #5? _____

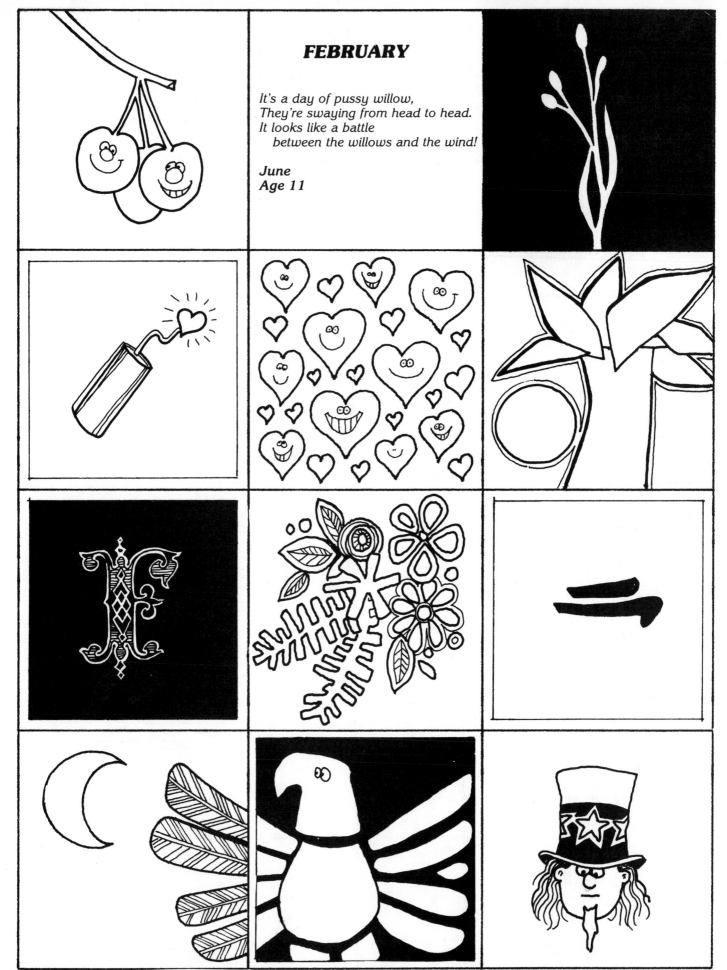

FEBRUARY

It's a day of pussy willow,
They're swaying from head to head.
It looks like a battle
*   between the willows and the wind!*

June
Age 11

From *Fragile as Butterflies* © Good Apple, Inc., 1983

61

February

Sunday	Monday	Tuesday	Wednesday	Thursday	Friday	Saturday

A. Run off enough calendars on the opposite page so that each student can have one of his own. You may also want to reproduce the cutouts found at the bottom of this page. The student can use these cutouts as "stickers" for his calendar. If one side of the pattern is put on the fold and the rest is cut out, the student can lift the pattern and write on the inside. These cutout "stickers" can be decorated as the student wishes. The cutout can be taped or glued to the appropriate place on the calendar.

The following activities are suggested uses for the calendar:

1. Each student can use the calendar as a cover for science work sheets. He can put a sticker on the calendar for each day he completes his science assignment. A "heart" report may also be included. The student can research the importance, function and parts of the heart. A good encyclopedia or science book would have this information.
2. Each student can put a cutout on the calendar for each day he said or did something nice for someone. An alternative is to have students exchange calendars with each other and keep track of the nice things the owner of that calendar has done during the month.

B. Enlarge the calendar (on the opposite page) to design a bulletin board for your classroom. An example is shown above. You may want students to complete ongoing activities to fill in the calendar. One student can be assigned to a specific day of the month. Some suggestions are given below. Enlarge the cutout patterns for students to write down the information they wish to place on the calendar. If one side of the pattern is put on the fold and the rest is cut out, the student can lift the pattern and write on the inside. These cutout "stickers" can be decorated as the student wishes. The cutout can be taped or glued to the appropriate place on the calendar.

Explain to students what Groundhog's Day is all about.
1. Have them check the groundhog's prediction by keeping track of the weather in February. On each day a different student can place an appropriate symbol telling whether the day was more like spring or winter.
2. Have a different student write a valentine sentiment for each day. These can be written on a cutout and glued or taped to the calendar.
3. Have students write down one reason why freedom is important for each day.

ACTIVITIES FOR FEBRUARY

BORN FREE

February 1 is designated as National Freedom Day. This is because in 1865 President Lincoln proposed the 13th Amendment to the U.S. Constitution—the antislavery amendment.

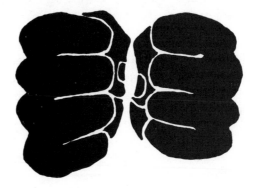

The words below relate to "Born Free." Fill in the final letter. Then write the meaning of the word in the blank.

1. **A**llegianc☐ _____

2. **B**ill of Right☐ _____

3. **C**onstitutio☐ _____

4. **D**emocrati☐ _____

5. **E**lectio☐ _____

6. **F**reedo☐ _____

7. **G**overnmen☐ _____

8. **H**eritag☐ _____

9. **I**ndependen☐ _____

10. **J**ur☐ _____

11. **K**nowledg☐ _____

12. **L**ibert☐ _____

13. **M**eetin☐ _____

14. **N**atio☐ _____

15. "**O**ld Glor☐" _____

16. **P**ledg☐ _____

17. **R**epubli☐ _____

18. **S**enat☐ _____

19. **T**axe☐ _____

20. **U**nio☐ _____

21. **V**ot☐ _____

WEATHER WATCH

February 2 is called Groundhog Day. Some people believe that if the groundhog comes out on that day and sees his shadow, winter will last six weeks longer.

Fill in the dates on the calendar below. Write your daily weather prediction for each day on the Groundhog Calendar below. Then record the real weather below it. Compare your predictions and the actual weather for each day. See how many come out to be the same.

GROUNDHOG CALENDAR

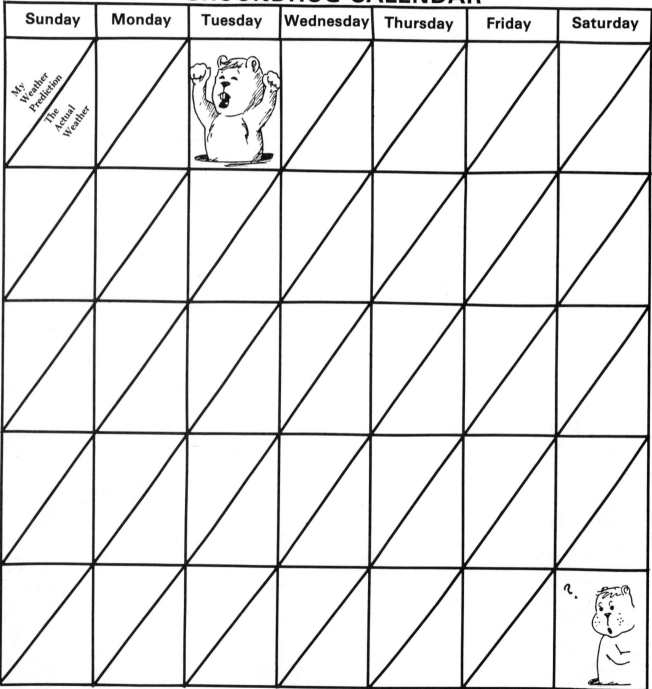

Sunday	Monday	Tuesday	Wednesday	Thursday	Friday	Saturday
My Weather Prediction / The Actual Weather						

On a separate sheet, make a Groundhog Weather Award which could be given to the best weather predictor in your class.

COINING NEW WORDS

On February 3, 1690, Massachusetts issued the first American paper money. This was to help pay soldiers for fighting in the war with Quebec. Before that, money was either gold or coins. There is another meaning for coining—the inventing of new words. Words coined recently are wire tapping, litterbug, graffiti, zip code, etc.

Match the following coined words:

a. ____ beardom

b. ____ vitamints

c. ____ bonette

d. ____ toyburg

e. ____ drencher

f. ____ smoochable

g. ____ candymania

h. ____ sockorama

i. ____ flippo

j. ____ weeplet

1. where toys live

2. kissable

3. a weak sob

4. a store where only socks are sold

5. candy vitamins

6. a craving for candy

7. a somersault

8. where bears hibernate

9. a little bone

10. a heavy rainstorm

Coin a few words of your own. You may want to use the "coin" endings. Be sure to tell what your new words mean.

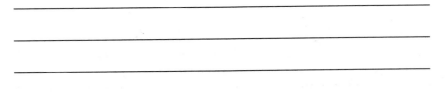

THE LONE EAGLE

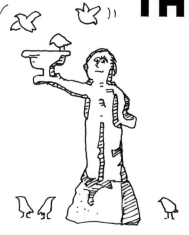

Charles Lindbergh was a famous pilot in American history. He was born February 4, 1902. He was known as the "Lone Eagle" for his pioneering solo flight across the Atlantic Ocean on May 20-21, 1927, in his plane named the *Spirit of St. Louis.* Charles Lindbergh's great flight across the Atlantic was 3,600 miles long, and it took him 33 hours and 32 minutes to fly the distance. Because of his bravery, he became the first American private citizen to become a public hero.

Read and answer the questions by putting a check mark in the yes or no column.

	Yes	No
	Y	M
1. Charles Lindbergh was a famous pilot.		
2. His plane was named the *Lone Eagle.*	b	o
3. He flew over the Pacific Ocean in 33 hours and 32 minutes.	t	u
4. Charles Lindbergh was born on February 4, 1902.	m	r
5. His solo flight was across the Atlantic Ocean.	a	u
6. The total distance of the flight was 36,000 miles.	i	d
7. The *Spirit of St. Louis* was the name of his plane.	e	m
8. Lindbergh became the first private citizen to become America's public hero.	i	s
9. Charles Lindbergh crossed the Atlantic on May 20 - 21, 1927.	t	d

Now go back and fill in the boxes below for the questions with the letters you checked in the yes and no columns.

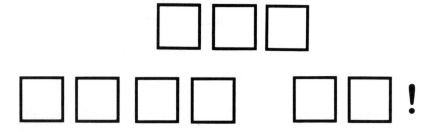

Figure the total minutes it took Lindbergh to fly across the Atlantic. How many miles did he travel per minute?

WINTER FUN

The first winter Olympic games were played in the United States on February 4, 1932. The winter Olympic games lasted about 12 days. Seven different sports were played in these games.

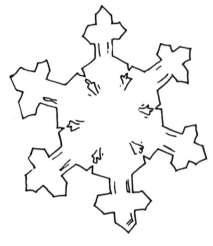

The dictionary lists words in alphabetical order. Read the winter Olympic games below and write them in alphabetical order.

1. skiing   1. _____

2. biathlon   2. _____

3. tobogganing   3. _____

4. bobsledding   4. _____

5. ice hockey   5. _____

6. speed skating   6. _____

7. figure skating   7. _____

1. Look up the sport *biathlon* and explain what it is. _____

_____

2. Which winter Olympic sport is your favorite? _____

_____

3. Write three sentences about your favorite winter sport. _____

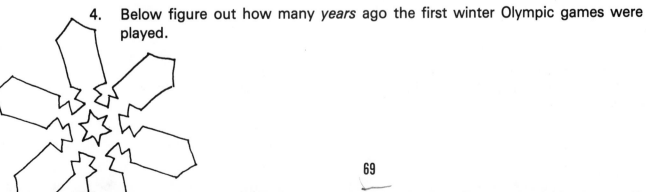

_____

_____

_____

_____

4. Below figure out how many *years* ago the first winter Olympic games were played.

AN ICY DOZEN

Figure skating is one of the sports used in the February winter Olympics. The world women's record is still held by Sonja Henie of Norway.

See if you can figure all the math on the ice pond of problems below. Then go back and color all the spaces blue which equal 12. It will tell you what every champion figure skater needs in order to win.

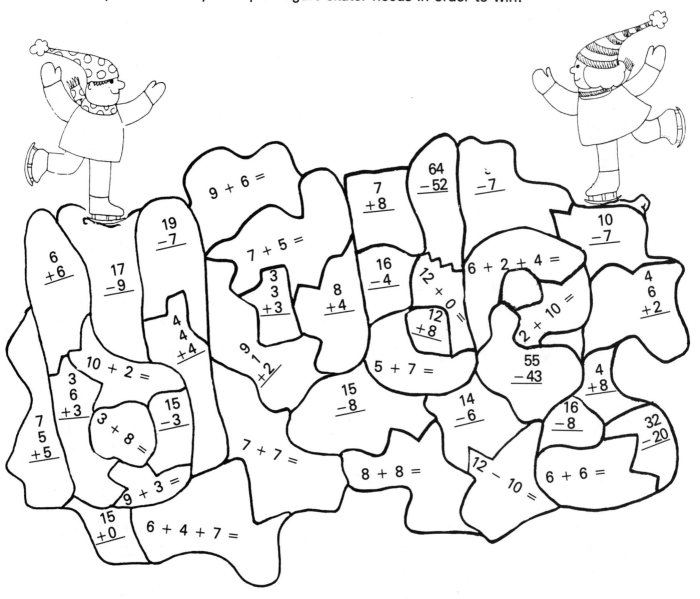

On the back of this sheet make a large figure ∞
Then make up five problems which would equal 8. Put them inside the figure.

MEDAL WINNERS

The top three athletes in each February winter Olympic event receive a medal and a certificate. The first place medal is gold, the second place medal is silver and the third place medal is bronze.

The chart below gives us information about four of the leading medal-winning nations in the 1980 winter Olympic games.

Nation	Gold	Silver	Bronze
East Germany	9	7	7
Soviet Union	10	6	6
United States	6	4	2
Norway	1	3	6

1. How many nations are represented in the chart? _____

2. How many gold medals were won by East Germany and Norway combined? __

3. Which nation won the most gold medals? _____

    Silver? _____   Bronze? _____

4. What is the total number of medals won by each nation?

    East Germany _____   United States _____

    Soviet Union _____   Norway _____

5. Give the total number of gold medals won by all four nations. _____

    Silver _____   Bronze _____

6. How many more medals were won by East Germany than Norway? _____

7. What is the total number of medals won by all four nations? _____

On the back, design your own special gold medal to give to someone you know. Also write what that person has done to deserve such an honor.

OOHH HENRY!

Henry "Hank" Aaron is a famous baseball player who was born in the month of February (February 5, 1934). He played for the Atlanta Braves and broke all records when he hit his 715th home run in 1974.

Some words have more than one meaning. On the line next to the sentence, write the letter of the explanation which means the same as the italicized word in the sentence.

On the back of this sheet, write two meanings for the words: *hit, out, drive.*

_____1. Her stocking had a *run* in it.
   a. to go faster than walking
   b. to ravel, broken stitches
   c. to cause to keep operating

_____2. The man slid in to second *base.*
   a. the lowest part of something
   b. one of four corners on a baseball diamond
   c. the main part of something

_____3. I will *bat* in the game.
   a. a wooden club
   b. to strike or hit
   c. a small, flying animal

_____4. The runner touched the *plate* before he was tagged with the ball.
   a. a flat dish
   b. a flat, thin piece of metal
   c. home plate in a baseball game

_____5. The *diamond* on her hand sparkled in the light.
   a. one shape on a playing card
   b. a crystal jewel
   c. space on a baseball field

_____6. Let's *pitch* some horseshoes.
   a. to throw or toss
   b. to set up
   c. to fall forward

_____7. The men at the mine planned a *strike.*
   a. to hit
   b. ceasing to work
   c. to cross out

_____8. The little girl almost fell off the *slide.*
   a. a slanted chute found on a playground
   b. a photograph that can be shown on a screen
   c. to move over the ground without losing contact with it

72

GEORGE HERMAN RUTH

George Herman Ruth was a famous baseball player. He was born February 6, 1895. He is remembered as the first great home run hitter in baseball history. He played for the New York Yankees and became one of the first five players elected to the National Baseball Hall of Fame.

Do the word puzzle below. Read the shaded boxes and it will tell you the well-known nickname of this famous player.

1. One of the four corners of a baseball diamond

2. A group of nine players playing together

3. To tap a baseball so it only goes a short distance

4. A ball that the batter swings at and misses

5. The record of points made in a game

6. Person who rules on plays in baseball

7. A shelter where baseball players sit when they are not playing

8. A ball thrown to a batter in baseball

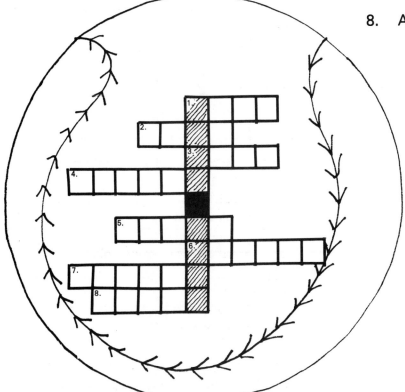

This player began his baseball career in 1914 and retired in 1935. How many years did he play baseball? _____ years

DO A GOOD DEED

The first Boy Scouts Day was on February 8, 1910. The Boy Scout pledge is:

"On my honor, I will do my best
To do my duty to God and my country, and
To obey the scout law
To help other people at all times
To keep myself physically strong, mentally awake,
And morally straight."

All the root words below need a suffix to make a new word. Do a good deed for yourself by making these new words and reading them.

Read the root words and new words' meanings. Then put a check ✓ in the chart to show the suffix needed to make a new word. Write the new word on the blank line. The first one is done for you.

Root Word	New Word Meaning	Suffixes				New Word
		ful	ness	able	ous	
help	giving help; useful	✓				helpful
kind	the habit of being kind					
agree	nice; pleasant and charming					
cheer	showing happiness					
fair	according to the rules					
courage	bravery; facing danger without fear					
care	paying close attention; watchful					
teach	able to be taught					
respect	having a good reputation					
humor	making people laugh; comical					
use	serving a good purpose					
honor	having a sense of what is right or honest					

On the back of this sheet, list two extra words having the suffixes of *ful, ness, able* and *ous.* Use two of them in sentences.

THE INVENTION FACTORY

Thomas Edison was one of the world's greatest inventors. He invented over 1,000 new inventions.

Because Edison asked so many questions, his teacher thought he was stupid. The teacher did not want to teach him. So Edison went to school at home.

He was very curious and studied history, stories and books about science. Edison wanted to know *why* and *how* about many things.

At ten years of age, Edison began working with chemicals and electrical current. At twelve years of age, Edison started his own candy and newspaper business.

When Edison was older, he opened his own *"Invention* Factory." Some of the 1,093 inventions of Edison included an improved electric *light bulb,* an improved *movie* camera and projector, and the *phonograph* (record player).

Edison said that *genius* was 99% perspiration and 1% inspiration. In other words, it takes *hard work* to make a good idea work.

Find the italicized words that are hidden in the puzzle. Circle them.

THOMAS A. EDISON
BORN: FEBRUARY 11, 1847

L	I	G	H	T	S	O
B	W	H	Y	H	O	W
U	I	E	G	O	N	P
L	N	O	E	M	E	H
B	V	W	N	A	M	O
S	E	D	I	S	O	N
O	N	I	U	N	V	O
H	T	N	S	A	I	G
A	I	E	T	T	E	R
R	O	O	T	E	S	A
D	N	O	E	S	E	P
W	O	R	K	H	A	H

On the back of this sheet, put the italicized words in alphabetical order.

THE PEOPLE'S CHOICE

Abraham Lincoln was born on February 12, 1809. Mr. Lincoln was elected President of the United States in 1860 and 1864. His friends called him "Honest Abe." Below are some statements that President Lincoln might have said during his presidency. Each sentence will have contractions italicized. At the end of each sentence, print the two words that make up the contraction.

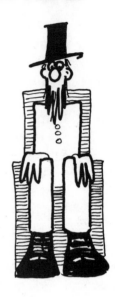

1. *Let's* be proud because the telegraph now extends across the country. _____ _____

2. When I choose my cabinet, *I'd* like Mr. Chase to be Secretary of the Treasury. _____ _____

3. *I've* often had problems with my cabinet. _____ _____

4. Although the Civil War takes up much of my time, I *mustn't* neglect my family. _____ _____

5. One of my plans is to blockade the southern states now that *they've* broken away from the Union. _____ _____

6. The war *didn't* go well for the first two years ... _____ _____

7. The victory at Gettysburg was the turning point, and it was fought after I declared, "The *time's* come to free the slaves." _____ _____

8. *Here's* a letter from General Grant saying that *Lee'll* surrender soon. _____ _____

_____ _____

9. *I'm* planning to relax now by attending a play at Ford's Theater. _____ _____

Choose one of the statements from above and research the events that would have led to the statement. Write these on the back.

ANIMATE THESE!

When we remember Abe Lincoln and celebrate his birthday, we often think of his great storytelling ability and speechmaking. Abraham Lincoln often used proverbs in his speeches. Below is a list of proverbs. Choose two and illustrate them in the boxes below.

1. Little pitchers have big ears.
2. A rolling stone gathers no moss.
3. If at first you don't succeed, try, try again.
4. He's a jack-of-all-trades, and master of none.
5. All that glitters is not gold.
6. A bird in the hand is worth two in the bush.
7. A penny saved is a penny earned.
8. A drop of honey catches more flies than a barrel of vinegar.
9. Actions speak louder than words.
10. Do unto others as you would have them do unto you.

Now choose either one of the proverbs you drew, a different one from the list, or make up one of your own. Write a story to go along with your proverb. You may have to use a separate sheet.

_____

_____

_____

_____

_____

_____

_____

DON'T WRIGGLE OUT OF THIS!

The first public school in America was established in Boston on February 13, 1635. The name of this school was The Boston Latin School. Although Abraham Lincoln did not have much opportunity to attend school 180 years later, he did like to study. He would never *wr*iggle out of this lesson using *wr* words where the *w* is always silent. He would probably complete it in seven minutes. Try matching his record.

1. Wrong is the opposite of ____   a. good person

2. Wrap is the opposite of ____   b. peace

3. Wrinkled is the opposite of ____   c. unwrap

4. Wrongdoer is the opposite of ____   d. right

5. Wrath is the opposite of ____   e. smooth

That was the warm-up. Match the following:

a. ____ wrangle   1. a timepiece strapped to the wrist

b. ____ writ   2. an unhappy person

c. ____ writhe   3. a sportsman

d. ____ wren   4. a ghost

e. ____ wrapper   5. a cover

f. ____ wretch   6. creases

g. ____ wristwatch   7. a legal document

h. ____ wrinkles   8. a small bird

i. ____ wrath   9. to squirm

j. ____ wrangler   10. a cowboy

k. ____ wraith   11. anger

l. ____ wring   12. argue

m. ____ wrench   13. a tool

n. ____ wrestler   14. to twist

78

A LOVER OF WORDS

February 14 is Valentine's Day in the United States. It is a day named in honor of Saint Valentine, an early Christian saint. It is celebrated by sending valentines and giving gifts of love.

Some valentine candy hearts have mini-messages printed on them. Read the words on the hearts below. Use at least five of these messages and write a make-believe conversation between two people or two animals. Write your conversation on the lines below. Be sure to use quotation marks and other punctuation marks properly.

My Pet · Now Now · Tell Me · How R-U · Be True · Good-bye · Maybe

Dream Girl · No Way · Don't Go · Trust Me · Hi Doll! · Stay Away · Smart Gal

Love Me · My Queen · Dream Boat · Some Day · Good Kid · My Star · Yes

_____

_____

_____

_____

_____

_____

_____

_____

_____

_____

_____

_____

THE MAINE

On February 15, 1898, the famous American battleship *Maine* was blown up in Havana, Cuba. The explosion killed 260 crew members and started the Spanish-American War. A famous slogan was spread throughout the United States during the war.

Solve the problems. Write the letters found by the problems above the matching sums in the box below. If you are correct, you can read the famous slogan.

A	B	C	D
563 +314	295 +684	439 +418	594 +287

E	F	G	H
542 +384	709 +112	197 +203	298 +594

I	J	K	L
483 +384	608 +172	440 +386	501 +107

M	N	O	P
586 +346	331 +226	572 +226	280 +572

R	S	T	U
781 +169	292 +427	295 +353	650 +278

___	___	___	___	___	___	___	___
950	926	932	926	932	979	926	950

___	___	___	___	___	___	___	___
648	892	926	932	877	867	557	926

!

On the back of this sheet, make up your own slogan with some new math problems and have a friend solve it.

"GUNG HO SUN HEE"

The Chinese New Year is celebrated anywhere between January 20 and February 20. People wish their friends "Gung Ho Sun Hee" and celebrate with food and festivities.

Read the word on each rice bowl below and the suffixes on the chopsticks. Choose a suffix from the chopsticks to complete each word. Write the new word on the line.

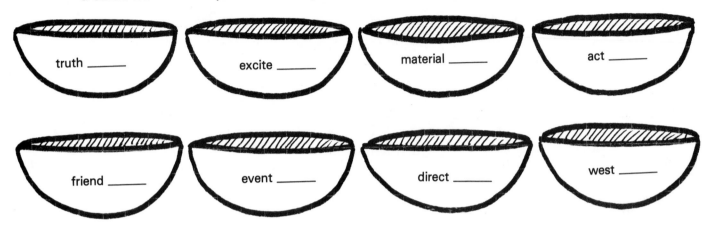

truth _____   excite _____   material _____   act _____

friend _____   event _____   direct _____   west _____

Directions: Read the word on each rice bowl below and the prefixes on the chopsticks. Choose a prefix from the chopsticks to complete each word and write it on the line.

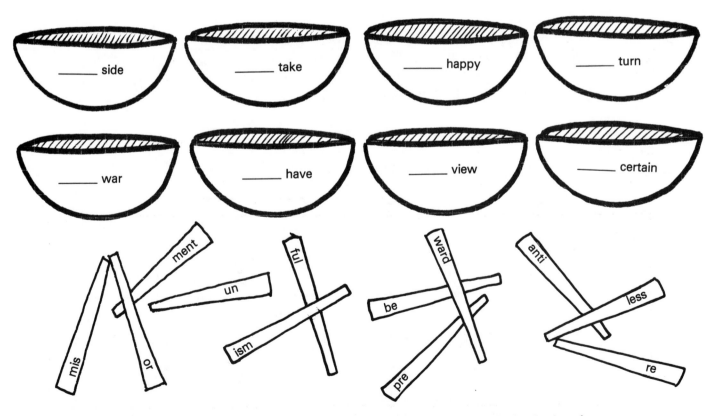

_____ side   _____ take   _____ happy   _____ turn

_____ war   _____ have   _____ view   _____ certain

On the back of this sheet, put all the new prefix words in alphabetical order.

CHINESE FACTS AND FIGURES

There are many interesting Chinese customs which can be seen during the Chinese New Year celebrations in February. During the New Year, the Chinese people honor their elders and families. Children are given gifts of money wrapped in red paper.

1. If someone received $3.75 in quarters, how many quarters would he have gotten?

   _____

Oranges are a Chinese symbol of good luck. Oranges are exchanged during New Year celebrations.

2. The heaviest orange in the world was grown by Bill Calendine of Tucson, Arizona. It weighed 3 lb. 11 oz. How many ounces did it weigh altogether?

   _____

3. If he sold this orange for 5¢ an ounce, how much would he receive for this orange?

   _____

A large paper dragon is usually found in every Chinese New Year parade. It is approximately 25 feet long and very colorful.

4. The longest float used in any street parade was a 200-foot-long dragon named Sun Loon. Six men were needed to carry its head alone. How many dragons could fit in this huge special dragon?

Chinese use these symbols to stand for various numbers:

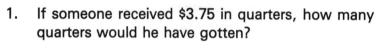

一 = 1	四 = 4	七 = 7
二 = 2	五 = 5	八 = 8
三 = 3	六 = 6	九 = 9
		十 = 10

5. Find the answer to the problem below:

四 + 五 + 六 − 十 × 五 + 八 + 二 + 五 = _____

On the back, make three problems using the Chinese symbols for numbers.

HAVE A COOKIE BREAK

Ancient Chinese sayings have lasted for many years. These sayings can be found in fortune cookies and tell the reader of good fortunes that may come to him in the future. Fortune cookies are given out to friends during the Chinese New Year.

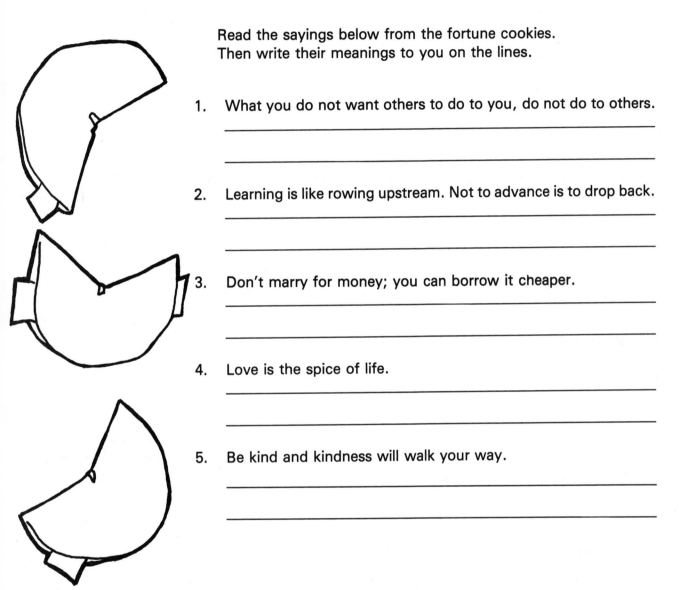

Read the sayings below from the fortune cookies.
Then write their meanings to you on the lines.

1. What you do not want others to do to you, do not do to others.
    _____
    _____

2. Learning is like rowing upstream. Not to advance is to drop back.
    _____
    _____

3. Don't marry for money; you can borrow it cheaper.
    _____
    _____

4. Love is the spice of life.
    _____
    _____

5. Be kind and kindness will walk your way.
    _____
    _____

On the back, write three fortunes you would like to grant a friend. Print them on a strip of paper and give them to the lucky person.

THE FRIENDSHIP 7

John Glenn was the first American to orbit the earth. He circled the earth three times in less than five hours on February 20, 1962. Millions of people watched on television as the spacecraft *Friendship 7* was carried into the sky by a giant Atlas rocket.

Final Countdown

John Glenn began his day at 2:20 a.m. when he had breakfast at Cape Canaveral. After breakfast he was checked over by doctors to see if he was ready for his trip into space. At 6:03 a.m., he climbed into his spacecraft to prepare for the final countdown. The countdown began at 6:25 a.m.

The sky cleared about 8:00 a.m. Millions of people watched the TV to see the huge rocket take John Glenn into space. At 9:42 a.m. John Glenn counted "...six, five, four, three, two, one, zero." The rocket rose into the sky. John Glenn had begun his flight into space.

Number the sentences in the correct order as they happened in the story.

_____ John Glenn climbed into the spacecraft.

_____ He ate breakfast at Cape Canaveral.

_____ At 9:42 a.m. John Glenn counted "... six, five, ..."

_____ The sky cleared.

_____ Doctors checked him over before flight.

_____ The rocket rose into the sky.

On the back of this sheet list the honors presented to John Glenn after his return from space. (You may want to use an encyclopedia.)

CALL ME!

The telephone was invented by Alexander Graham Bell. At that time, Mr. Bell was the only one with a telephone. Now millions of people own telephones. How do we know which number to call for each person?

Use the code below and you will know the answer.

Example: 7_1 would be P, 5_2 would be K. The first word is done for you.

	ABC	DEF
1	2	3
GHI	JKL	MNO
4	5	6
PRS	TUV	WXY
7	8	9
	0	

RING RING

O n __ __ __ __ __ __ __ __   21, 1878, __ __ __

6_3 6_2 3_3 3_2 2_2 7_2 8_2 2_1 7_2 9_3 8_1 4_2 3_2

__ __ __ __ __ __ __ __ __ __ __ __ __

3_3 4_3 7_2 7_3 8_1 8_1 3_2 5_3 3_2 7_1 4_2 6_3 6_2 3_2

__ __ __ __ __ __ __ __ __ __ __ __ __ __ __ __ __

2_2 6_3 6_3 5_2 9_1 2_1 7_3 2_3 4_3 7_2 2_3 8_2 5_3 2_1 8_1 3_2 3_1

__ __ __ __ __ __ __ __ __ __ __

4_3 6_2 8_1 4_2 3_2 8_2 6_2 4_3 8_1 3_2 3_1

__ __ __ __ __ __ .

7_3 8_1 2_1 8_1 3_2 7_3

On the back of this sheet, make your own coded message for a friend to solve.

YOUR FINGERS DO THE WALKING

Our phone book has seen many changes since February 21, 1878. Open to any page in the white pages of a phone book. Notice the two words at the top of the page. These are guide words. The word on the left tells you the first name on the page. The word on the right tells you the last name on the page.

When you are looking for a name, you don't have to read all the names on a page. Look at the guide words, and they will tell you if the name is on the page.

Here is a page from the telephone book. Use the guide words to answer the questions below. Write "yes" if the word belongs on the page below. Write "no" if the word does not belong on the page.

LAR—LIM

Larkin J 913 Jamie Ln	837-1615
Larner Francis W	
426 Summers Dr	833-5286
Larner Russell D 915 W Adams	833-5372
Larry Graves Machine Shop 121 N Bonham	837-4488
Leftrook Nicholas Pastor 1030 Derry Ln	833-4010
Legg Henry J 100 Arlington Dr	837-1862
Legg John 345 Jamestown Rd	837-6386
Leggett A M 336 S McArthur	837-2584
Legh–Page Jas D	
1 Lamoine Village	836-9951
Lehman Nora L 1030-31 Derry Ln	837-1212
Leigh Elma M 70 S Yorktown	837-2751
Liljegren Robert E 1587 Riverview	833-3479
Lillie Dennis 432 ½ N Pearl	833-3221
Lilly Jamie 1400 University Dr	833-5090
Limkeman Kim A 3 Lamoine Village	837-4667
Limkeman Tim 1545 Riverview Dr	833-3253
Limper Scott 1025 ½ E Elm	837-6279

Lake _____   Loxon _____   Larkin _____

Luper _____   Lehman _____   Lillins _____

Luft _____   Lester _____   Lelton _____

What is the first name on this page? _____

What is the last name on this page? _____

Make up 5 names that would belong on this telephone page. List them here. _____

_____

_____

The Yellow Pages are another part of the telephone book. On the back of this page, make up an ad that could be in the Yellow Pages. Make if funny if you want and make a serious one, too.

NATIONAL WILDLIFE WEEK

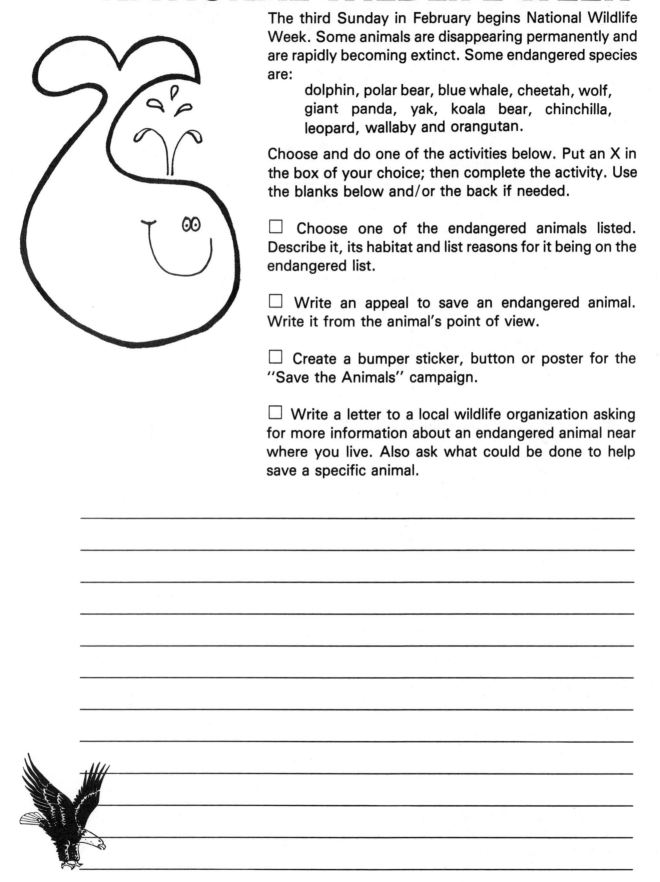

The third Sunday in February begins National Wildlife Week. Some animals are disappearing permanently and are rapidly becoming extinct. Some endangered species are:

> dolphin, polar bear, blue whale, cheetah, wolf, giant panda, yak, koala bear, chinchilla, leopard, wallaby and orangutan.

Choose and do one of the activities below. Put an X in the box of your choice; then complete the activity. Use the blanks below and/or the back if needed.

☐ Choose one of the endangered animals listed. Describe it, its habitat and list reasons for it being on the endangered list.

☐ Write an appeal to save an endangered animal. Write it from the animal's point of view.

☐ Create a bumper sticker, button or poster for the ''Save the Animals'' campaign.

☐ Write a letter to a local wildlife organization asking for more information about an endangered animal near where you live. Also ask what could be done to help save a specific animal.

_____

_____

_____

_____

_____

_____

_____

_____

_____

GEORGE WASHINGTON, 'TIS FOR THEE!

February 22 is George Washington's birthday. He was born in 1732. How old would he be today?

_____
years old

The following were all named for George Washington. Match them.

____ 1.   Washington, D.C.

____ 2.   Washington's birthday

____ 3.   "Bow down to Washington"

____ 4.   Washington Memorial Arch

____ 5.   Washington elm

____ 6.   Washington Monument

____ 7.   Washington & Lee University

____ 8.   George Washington Carver

____ 9.   Booker T. Washington

____10.   Washington Post

____11.   Mount Washington

____12.   Washington

____13.   George Washington Custis

____14.   Washington Co.

____15.   Washingtonia

____16.   Washingtonians

A.   a school song of Washington University

B.   a school named for Washington and a Southern general

C.   a high peak in New Hampshire

D.   a kind of palm named for Washington

E.   a great tree under which Washington took command of the American army

F.   capital city of the U.S.A.

G.   a famous educator who was once a slave

H.   residents of Washington, D.C.

I.   a freed slave who became a great scientist

J.   a legal holiday in the U.S.A. (February 22)

K.   a great obelisk over 555 feet high

L.   the only state named for a president

M.   a Pennsylvania county named for Washington

N.   Washington's adopted son

O.   a newspaper

P.   a curved span that is the entrance to Washington Square, New York City

On the back, list other things that could have been named after George Washington. Are some of these things in your area?

WELCOME TO THE UNION

February is sometimes called the patriotism month because we remember our country and how it began. Two of our present states were admitted to the Union during the month of February.

Color in each word below having a long vowel. Look carefully and it will tell you when Arizona became a state.

green	grub	plain	play	strap	plead	stem	rent	tray	pelt
dream	speak	deck	east	grin	flies	plum	braid	crept	steep
clay	toast	peck	stray	spend	pleat	spend	stun	slum	brain
waist	stump	free	flea	slant	cream	press	drip	dried	wed
claim	crept	click	cues	film	groan	hint	cloak	swept	drift
float	bless	blend	sheet	speck	greet	grip	hued	plump	weld
speed	task	drift	stain	swell	fried	cluck	speech	fleet	least

Color in each word below having a silent letter. Look carefully and it will tell you when Oregon became a state.

wrote	ship	often	champ	pitch	bomb	dodge	fled	wring	eight
knee	limb	gush	walk	witch	prop	wilt	stalk	trap	nigh
tight	ridge	blob	knack	knit	wrath	stunt	would	trust	ledge
yolk	raft	wrist	blunt	should	bulb	balm	crop	talk	notch
ditch	half	grasp	tomb	west	scalp	flight	swam	blot	castle
edge	high	wept	calf	calm	suds	wren	flip	elf	crumb
comb	plot	might	crisp	strip	folks	slam	win	clod	hatch

On the back of this sheet, make a puzzle of your own. Try to do the year you were born. Use short vowel words. Give it to a friend to do.

AN EXTRA DAY

Leap Year has 366 days, or one more day than an ordinary year. The extra day is added to the end of February and becomes February 29th every four years.

Read the code below and fill in the number table.

L = 1 E = 2 A = 3 P = 4   Y = 5 E = 2 A = 3 R = 6

+	L	E	A	P	Y	E	A	R
L								
E		4				4		
A								
P								
Y								
E		4				4		
A								
R								

On the back of this sheet, make a number table for a friend to solve.